THE BRE: FOOTBALL QUIZ BOOK

Written by Chris Coley and Bill Edgar

All profits from the sale of this book will go to The Jeff Astle Foundation

Copyright © Chris Coley and Bill Edgar 2023
ISBN 978-1-3999-6336-7

Printed and bound by:
LPD, Greenway House, Sugarwell Business Park
Shenington, Banbury, Oxfordshire OX15 6HW

Typesetting and Design by:
Amy Leat, iPlus Group

The authors would like to thank the following:
Mark Brereton, Stephen Chalke, Paul Clixby, Marc Cutler, Carla Draper, Teddy Draper,
Michael-John Jennings, Susanna Kendall, Dominic Perry, Graham Stone & Nathaly Turner.

The authors would like to acknowledge the following for their photographs:
The Times newspaper
David Sheilds / footballstadiumphotography.co.uk
Ian Mulcahy / iansapps.co.uk

First Published 2023.
All answers have been researched as correct at 8th September 2023.
Any errors are the responsibility of the authors.

FOREWORD BY
ALAN SHEARER

When I retired from football, I knew there was a good chance my playing days would lead to health problems in later life. Dodgy knees, bad ankles, aching back; I was ready. But what I hadn't expected was that playing the game I loved could give me a higher chance of developing dementia.

It makes sense, right?

If you play for 20 years and head the ball in training up to 100 times a day, it must take a toll. Research published in 2019 found that former professional footballers are three and a half times more likely to die with dementia than the general population.

What I found hardest, on my journey to understand the link between football and dementia, was meeting former players affected by the disease. It's devastating. And it's not just them. It affects their families too.

I'm pleased that changes are starting to be made: professional footballers are now limited to 10 'high force headers' a week in training, and children under 12 are not taught to head a football during training. But more research and more change is needed to make the game we all love, safer for everyone.

That's why I'm so proud to be a patron of The Jeff Astle Foundation.

Jeff, who played for West Bromwich

Albion and England, was diagnosed with dementia at only 55 years old. Sadly he passed away just 4 years later in 2002, aged 59. At the inquest into his death, the coroner said the damage to Jeff's brain had been caused by years of heading a football.

The Foundation's aims are to support former players diagnosed with dementia along with their families, to educate about the long term and short term risks of repeated head impacts and to lobby for meaningful and timely research.

So, I'm delighted that all the profits from The BresBet Football Quiz Book will be donated to the Foundation's amazing work.

And what better way than a football quiz to help keep your brain healthy?!

Alan Shearer
Patron of The Jeff Astle Foundation

ABOUT THE AUTHORS

CHRIS COLEY

BILL EDGAR

Chris Coley has been well known in the Gloucestershire sporting circles since his days at Cheltenham College and has played cricket, rugby and football for Cheltenham.

He has been actively involved in sport quizzing since the late 1960s and appeared on the BBC's Brain of Sport programme, hosted by Peter Jones, in the early 1970s.

Since lockdown Chris has published a series of sporting quiz books with all proceeds going to various sporting charities. A catalogue of his books can be found at greatquizbooks.co.uk.

Bill Edgar has written about football for The Times since 1997, having initially worked for the Eastern Daily Press in Norfolk, for Today in London, and for the Cape Argus in Cape Town.

After spending many years on the road covering matches and press conferences, he now takes a statistical overview of the game.

He is the author of Bill Edgar's Quirky Football Quiz Book, and Back of the Net – 100 Golden Goals; he also co-authored A Football Fan's Guide to Europe.

The Jeff Astle Foundation

An ordinary man with an extraordinary talent.

In 2002, the tragic death of Jeff Astle, aged just 59, and the findings that were made post-mortem, raised serious concerns for the game of football and sport in general.

Jeff was known for his outstanding footballing career. Leading goal scorer in the old 1st Division in the 1969-70 season, a member of Sir Alf Ramsey's 1970 World Cup squad, the first player to score a goal in a League Cup final and an FA Cup final at Wembley Stadium and scoring the winning goal in the WBA v Everton 1968 FA Cup final where he became one of only 12 players in the history of the competition to score a goal in every round, including the final.

Sadly, at the age of only 55, Jeff was diagnosed with dementia, early onset Alzheimer's Disease. He died 4 years later at the age of only 59 on the 19th of January 2002.

In November of that year, Jeff's family attended The Coroners Court. A pathologist described the considerable amount of trauma to his brain, which was similar to that of a boxer. He said the main candidate for this trauma was heading footballs and it was the repeated heading of footballs throughout his footballing career that appeared to be the problem.

H.M Coroner Mr Andrew Haig said "Mr Astle's type of dementia is entirely consistent with heading footballs and his occupational exposure has made a significant contribution to the disease which has caused his death."

The verdict..... Industrial Disease, in other words, Jeff's job had killed him.
This was a landmark ruling.

Jeff's family were heartened by the news that Footballs Authorities appeared to be taking this seriously after they announced they were conducting a 10-year study looking at the links between heading balls and Neuro Degenerative Diseases. They assumed, incorrectly, that a ruling by HM Coroner of Industrial Disease would be a defining moment and the sport would act with vigour to both protect future generations of footballers and help those past heroes who were dying.

They assumed, again incorrectly, that the research that started in 2001, which was funded by The FA and The PFA, would address the two most obvious questions; How many former footballers have got dementia and is the game safe now?

It answered neither.

Nothing was published, no one had the courtesy to tell the Astle family. It was now 12 years after Jeff had died, and the issue was no further forward.

So, in 2014, the Astle family, with the help of West Bromwich Albion supporters, started a campaign, 'Justice for Jeff'.

A 25ft banner was held up on the 9th minute of all WBA matches accompanied by a minute's applause. The campaign was gathering momentum. Local then national TV, radio and newspapers, the banner was talked about during live Sky Sports games and by Match of the Day commentators. Finally, the FA sat up and listened and the Astle family were invited to meet with the then Chairman of The FA, Greg Dyke.

In 2018 Dr Willie Stewart began 'The Field Study'.

We now know that our **professional footballers are 5x more likely to die with Alzheimer's Disease** than you and I.

A very unsettling and uncomfortable reality.

A continuation of this data also showed that a footballer's playing position and length of playing career is tied to higher Neuro Degenerative Disease risk.

So, the risk of dementia in former players varies by player position and career length, not by player era, and not by the old leather ball because this increased risk was the same for those former players who never played with the old ball.

In 2014, Jeff's family asked that his brain be re-examined after they became aware of a disease called Chronic Traumatic Encephalopathy, a degenerative brain disease caused by multiple concussions or repeated sub concussive blows. It was found that Jeff didn't have Alzheimer's Disease. He was now the first British footballer to have died with CTE.

The Astle family wanted to create a lasting legacy for Jeff and for past, current and future players by establishing a Charity in his name. On April 11th 2015, the family launched
The Jeff Astle Foundation.

The Charity has 3 principal aims:

» Support for players and their families

» Education and Awareness of the dangers of both short term and long-term head impacts and injury

» Independent research

Jeff's death, and the death of so many former footballers, matter; they all matter.

The Astle family are proud that, although dementia robbed Jeff of his life far too soon, it gave them the strength and the ability to start the discussions around dementia and Neuro Degenerative diseases in the game.

The Jeff Astle Foundation
thejeffastlefoundation.co.uk

THE ROUNDS

CONTENTS

THE ROUNDS
CONTENTS

FIRST IMPRESSIONS

Notable first games

1   Against which club did Alan Shearer score a hat-trick for Southampton on the first senior start of his career in 1988?

2   Tottenham Hotspur's 10-4 victory at home to Everton in 1958 – the highest-scoring match in top-flight history – was also whose first game as Tottenham manager?

3   In September 1999 Newcastle United beat Sheffield Wednesday 8-0 in the Premier League in the first home game overseen by which new Newcastle manager?

4   Dave Sexton's first game as Coventry City manager in August 1981 – a 2-1 home win over Manchester United, who had sacked him that summer – was also notable for what footballing first in England?

5   Which Middlesbrough and Italy striker scored a hat-trick against Liverpool in 1996 on his debut in English football?

6   Bolton Wanderers drew 0-0 in the first match played at their new Reebok Stadium in September 1997, when the video replay showed they should have won because an effort by Bolton's Gerry Taggart had crossed the goalline. They were subsequently relegated because they lost out on goal difference to their opponents on that day. Name that team.

7   Which club lost 7-4 at home to Crewe Alexandra on the first League appearance in their history in 1991?

8   Which England defender scored an own goal and was sent off on his Real Madrid debut in 2005?

9   England were thrashed 5-2 by which nation in Sir Alf Ramsey's first match as manager in 1963?

10   Who scored a hat-trick against Newcastle United in 1988 in his first match for Everton after moving from West Ham United?

THE NAME IS THE SAME

Identify the common surname for these two players

1   (a) Played as a full back for Ipswich Town in the 1981 Uefa Cup final.
     (b) Played as a full back for Leeds United in the Champions League semi-finals in 2001.

2   (a) Welsh midfielder who appeared for Liverpool in the 2016 Europa League final.
     (b) Striker who played in FA Cup finals for Tottenham Hotspur (in 1987) and against them for Queens Park Rangers (in 1982).

3   (a) Left England's 2022 World Cup squad during the tournament for personal reasons.
     (b) Retired in 2022 when England women's record goalscorer.

4   (a) Premier League's top scorer in 1999-2000 with 30 goals for Sunderland.
     (b) Welsh midfielder who finished third in the Premier League with both Norwich City in 1992-93 and Nottingham Forest in 1994-95.

5   (a) Left-footed winger who appeared for England in the 1980s, and played for Manchester City and Manchester United.
     (b) Left-winger who appeared for England in the 1980s, and played for Watford in the 1984 FA Cup final.

6   (a) Welshman who is a legend at Juventus.
     (b) Nottingham Forest player on the end of a bad foul by Paul Gascoigne in the 1991 FA Cup final that injured the latter.

7   (a) Liverpool player nicknamed "Crazy Horse".
     (b) Manchester United player nicknamed "Sparky".

8   (a) Scored for Chelsea in the 1997 FA Cup final.
     (b) Everton defender who played for England at the 1970 World Cup.

9   (a) Named in 1977 as the PFA's Players' Player of the Year and Young Player of the Year.
     (b) Winger who was player and manager at Leeds United.

10   (a) Player whose winning goal for Oldham Athletic against Aston Villa in 1993 handed Manchester United their first League title since 1967.
     (b) Frenchman who was the Premier League's top scorer four times in the space of five seasons.

STARTING POINTS

Match the player to the League club for which he made his first senior appearance

1	Kevin Keegan		**A**	Exeter City
2	Dele Alli		**B**	Chesterfield
3	David Seaman		**C**	Bury
4	Lee Sharpe		**D**	Southport
5	David Platt		**E**	Peterborough United
6	Phil Neal		**F**	Barnsley
7	Steve Bruce		**G**	Bolton Wanderers
8	Ollie Watkins		**H**	Northampton Town
9	John Stones		**I**	Leyton Orient
10	Gordon Banks		**J**	Scunthorpe United
11	Harry Kane		**K**	Gillingham
12	Terry McDermott		**L**	Shrewsbury Town
13	Joe Hart		**M**	Milton Keynes Dons
14	Peter Reid		**N**	Torquay United
15	Peter Withe		**O**	Crewe Alexandra

HAPPY FAMILIES (PART 1)

Questions relating to footballing families

1   Frank Lampard Snr and Frank Lampard Jnr won a combined 108 England caps – how many of those did Frank Lampard Snr win?

2   One brother scored the BBC's Goal of the Season in 1979-80 when playing for Norwich City against Liverpool; the other brother helped Wimbledon beat Liverpool in the 1988 FA Cup final. Name those brothers.

3   Angus Gunn was Southampton's unfortunate goalkeeper when they lost 9-0 to a Leicester City side with Kasper Schmeichel in goal in 2019, but for which clubs were their fathers playing in goal when they met five times in the top division in the 1990s?

4   Brian Clough and his son Nigel both managed which club?

5   Which brother and sister were both playing for Chelsea in 2023?

6   When Liverpool's Steven Gerrard faced his cousin Anthony Gerrard in the 2012 League Cup final which team was facing the Merseyside club?

7   When Stoke City met York City in a League game in 1998 which two brothers and former Aston Villa players were the opposing managers?

8   Who played for Norwich City and Manchester City when his father was manager?

9   The Tottenham Hotspur defender Cyril Knowles – after whom the song 'Nice One Cyril' was written – had a brother who played for Wolverhampton Wanderers but retired aged 24 to concentrate on his life as a Jehovah's Witness. Name the brother.

10   Which goalkeeper won the League title with Ipswich Town in 1962 and then saw his son, also a goalkeeper, win the FA Cup twice with Manchester United?

ROUND 5
RESTRICTED VIEWS

Identify the home club from the unusual camera angle

Photos courtesy of footballstadiumphotography.co.uk and iansapps.co.uk

ROUND 6

HOLY ORDERS

Questions with a "religious" theme

1   Vicarage Road is the home to Watford FC but which Premiership rugby union club played its home games there from 1997-2013?

2   Who, in March 2021, became the first goalkeeper not to concede a goal in his first six appearances for England?

3   The Liverpool-born Rabbi Matondo, who was appearing for Rangers in 2023, plays international football for which home nation?

4   Who made more than 600 Leicester City appearances and also played as an all-rounder for Leicestershire County Cricket Club?

5   Who scored Everton's winning goal in the 1966 FA Cup final a year after winning his only England cap?

6   Which Everton forward scored 60 League goals in 1927-28, a record in one season?

7   Which club, based in County Durham, won the FA Amateur Cup a record ten times, twice as many as any other team?

8   The French goalkeeper Bernard Lama had a brief spell on loan to which London club?

9   The Scottish winger Owen Archdeacon played for Celtic and also spent seven years at which Yorkshire club from 1989?

10   Islam Slimani, the Algerian forward, played for which English club in the Champions League in 2016-17?

CELEBRITY FANS

Match the club to their well-known supporter

1	Arsenal	A	Jarvis Cocker
2	Southampton	B	Adele
3	Everton	C	Jasper Carrott
4	Sunderland	D	Usain Bolt
5	Birmingham City	E	Russell Crowe
6	Tottenham Hotspur	F	Bill Nighy
7	Leeds United	G	Judi Dench
8	Chelsea	H	Jessica Ennis-Hill
9	Sheffield United	I	Tim Rice
10	Fulham	J	Hugh Grant
11	Manchester City	K	Idris Elba
12	Crystal Palace	L	Noel Gallagher
13	West Ham United	M	Michael Caine
14	Manchester United	N	Craig David
15	Sheffield Wednesday	O	James Corden

MEDIA MATTERS

Famous quotes from microphone and print

1   Name the BBC television commentator at the 1966 World Cup final who said: "Some people are on the pitch; they think it's all over. It is now."

2   When Brian Moore, the ITV commentator, said "It's up for grabs now" at Anfield in May 1989 which player proceeded to score Arsenal's title-winning goal against Liverpool?

3   Which England manager was the Daily Mirror addressing when, after a poor performance against Saudi Arabia in 1988, its headline read: "Go, in the name of Allah, go"?

4   Name the player who scored Manchester United's late equaliser against Bayern Munich at a corner in the 1999 Champions League final shortly after ITV commentator Clive Tyldesley had said: "Can Manchester United score? They always score."

5   Which teams were in opposition in the 1988 FA Cup final when John Motson, the BBC television commentator, said after the final whistle: "The Crazy Gang have beaten the Culture Club"?

6   What was the vegetable-related headline in The Sun newspaper after England were knocked out of Euro 1992 by a 2-1 defeat to Sweden?

7   In the 1974 FA Cup final between Liverpool and Newcastle United which BBC television commentator responded to a goal by Liverpool's Kevin Keegan by saying: "Goals pay the rent, and Keegan does his share"?

8   To which red-carded England player was the Daily Mirror referring when, after the defeat on penalties to Argentina at the 1998 World Cup, its headline read: "Ten heroic Lions, one stupid boy"?

9   Which BBC radio commentator said "And Smith must score" when Brighton & Hove Albion's Gordon Smith had a chance to score a late winning goal in the 1983 FA Cup final against Manchester United (a chance that he failed to convert)?

10   Which Derby County player scored the winning goal away to his former club Manchester City in December 1974, prompting the BBC television commentator Barry Davies to say: "Just look at his face"?

DICTIONARY DEFINITIONS

Identify the player from their main club (most games played) and years spent there, along with the definition of their surname

1   (a) Leeds, 1989-96.
    (b) "Rate of motion of progress."

2   (a) Stoke, 2011-19.
    (b) "To stoop or bend low."

3   (a) Man Utd, 1992-2004.
    (b) "To strike or push with the head or horns."

4   (a) Leicester, 1997-2002.
    (b) "Fierce, ferocious or cruel."

5   (a) Arsenal, 1990-2003.
    (b) "A person who helps in the handling, sailing and navigating of a ship during a voyage."

6   (a) Wimbledon, 1987-94.
    (b) "A set of notes played or sung in order, going up or down."

7   (a) Chelsea, 1990-2001.
    (b) "Judicious or prudent."

8   (a) Leeds, 1987-1993; 1998-2004.
    (b) "Insane, crazy, eccentric."

9   (a) Liverpool, 1959-69.
    (b) "To pursue with force, hostility."

10 (a) Fulham, 1952-61.
    (b) "A natural elevation of the earth's surface, smaller than a mountain."

11 (a) Wigan Athletic, 2016-18.
    (b) "Produce flames and heat while consuming a material."

12 (a) West Bromwich Albion, 2011-18.
    (b) "Encourage the development of something."

DOUBLE FIGURES

Teams who scored ten or more goals in a match

1   Which club beat Anderlecht 10-0 in their first ever home match in European competition in 1956?

2   Paul Stewart, David White and Tony Adcock each scored a hat-trick for which team as they beat Huddersfield Town 10-1 in a League game in November 1987?

3   Which team had beaten Chesterfield 10-0 in a League fixture just two months before the match mentioned in question two?

4   Which London club won 10-0 at home to Bury in a League Cup match in 1983?

5   Ted MacDougall scored nine goals for which club in their 11-0 win over Margate in the FA Cup in 1971?

6   Which club beat Norwegian team SFK Lyn 10-0 in a European Cup match in 1969?

7   Which Welsh club did Newcastle United beat 13-0 in the second tier in 1946 – the joint biggest victory in League history?

8   In the first five League seasons the only teams to score more than ten are both known as the Magpies – Newcastle United and which other club?

9   Liverpool beat which London team 10-0 in a League Cup match in 1986?

10 Gerry Hitchens scored five goals for which club in their 11-1 win over Charlton Athletic in 1959?

MAPPING IT OUT

Identify the footballer whose surname matches the town or city indicated

1   Scored the winning goal for Arsenal in the 1979 FA Cup final.

2   Promotion-winner with Cambridge United and title winner with Manchester United.

3   First manager to lead England to a European Championship final.

4   Professional Footballers' Association chairman who played for Burnley.

5   Won the League title six times as Liverpool manager.

6   Centre back who played for Wales in the Euro 2016 semi-finals.

7   Blackburn Rovers and Chelsea striker who is a BBC pundit.

8   Had two spells with Crystal Palace and managed Notts County and Cambridge United.

9   Goalkeeper who gained promotions to the top flight with Leicester City in 1994 and 1996.

10   Left back who won the FA Cup and League Cup with Tottenham Hotspur in the 1990s.

11   Left-footed winger who completed ten seasons with Brighton & Hove Albion in 2023.

12   Goalkeeper who won League title with Everton in 1985 and 1987.

13   Striker who played in all four League divisions with Wimbledon.

14   Blackburn Rovers player who played for England at the 1958 and 1962 World Cups.

15   Midfielder who played for Fulham in the 1975 FA Cup final.

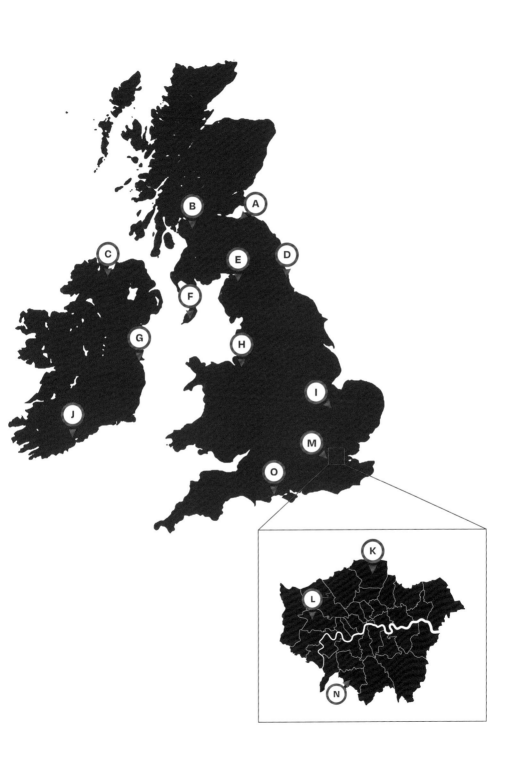

BLUE BLOODS

Questions with a royal or noble theme

1 Which club became champions in a season when they fielded an Andy King and played home games at the King Power Stadium?

2 Who were known as the Biscuitmen but now have a nickname of the Royals?

3 Who played in goal for Liverpool in the 2007 Champions League final defeat to AC Milan and has a surname that means "queen" in Spanish?

4 John Marquis scored 26 League goals to help which Yorkshire club gain promotion to the third tier in 2017?

5 What is the name of the controversial Burnley chairman who died in 1981 and who has a stand at the club's Turf Moor ground named after him?

6 Matt Duke was sent off while playing in goal for which fourth-tier club in the 2013 League Cup final?

7 Which local boy played in 18 consecutive seasons for West Ham United before retiring in 2022?

8 Kevin Baron played for which North West club in their FA Cup final defeat to Arsenal in 1950?

9 Which goalkeeper made more than 800 appearances for Portsmouth?

10 Gerry Queen played as a forward in the top division for which club in the early 1970s?

MEET THE SMITHS

Give the first name of each Smith

1 Arsenal striker who was the top flight's leading goalscorer as his team won the title in both 1988-89 and 1990-91.

2 Englishman who managed Wales in spells in the 1970s and 1990s.

3 Which woman, famed for her culinary skills, held, until early in the 2023-24 season, a joint majority shareholding in Norwich City?

4 Forward who top-scored for Tottenham Hotspur when they won the double in 1960-61.

5 Born on Merseyside, she won 93 caps with the England women's team and appears regularly as a pundit on Sky Sports.

6 Won promotions as manager of Colchester United, Birmingham City, Oxford United and Derby County.

7 Yorkshireman who played for Leeds United in a Champions League semi-final in 2001 and for Manchester United in a Champions League quarter-final in 2007.

8 Defender who surprisingly scored in Liverpool's European Cup final win over Borussia Monchengladbach in 1977.

9 A striker with Arsenal Women who scored 46 goals for England.

10 Aston Villa fan who guided the club to promotion to the Premier League as manager in 2019.

IT TAKES ALL SPORTS

Football's links to other sports

1 Curtis Woodhouse played in the Premier League with Birmingham City but later began a career in which other sport?

2 Who appeared for six London clubs and then played American football for the London Monarchs?

3 Who scored 21 goals in 46 England appearances and then became a leading racehorse trainer?

4 Which legendary England winger had a son who became a Wimbledon Junior tennis champion?

5 Which former Chelsea goalkeeper joined the Guildford Phoenix ice hockey team as goaltender in 2019?

6 The annual Oxford v Cambridge Boat Race passes close to which League ground?

7 Which ground was Derby County's home for more than a hundred years?

8 Which racehorse, co-owned by former Manchester United manager Sir Alex Ferguson, was the first to win seven consecutive Group One races in the Northern Hemisphere?

9 Of which footballer was it said that his priorities were the Welsh national team, golf and Real Madrid, in that order?

10 Which footballer, who won an England cap in 1901, also equalled the world long jump record?

ROUND 15

GENERAL KNOWLEDGE

Name the player (whose main club is given) with a surname matching that of a famous person, place or company

1   (a) Chelsea, 1998-2017.
     (b) Chocolate maker founded in York in 1767.

2   (a) Arsenal, 1988-2002.
     (b) The central character of a TV series famous for its opening line "Evening all" and closing line "Goodnight all".

3   (a) Middlesbrough, 2002-09, 2015-19.
     (b) Street housing British Prime Minster's main residence.

4   (a) Manchester United, 2002-14.
     (b) Man whose assassination in Sarajevo is considered the immediate cause of the First World War.

5   (a) Blackburn Rovers, 1992-99.
     (b) A forest in Nottinghamshire associated with an heroic outlaw.

6   (a) Aston Villa, 1998-2009.
     (b) A Welsh resort once home to a Butlins Holiday Camp.

7   (a) Tottenham Hotspur, 1992-2001.
     (b) American soup company founded in 1869.

8   (a) Liverpool, 1987-97.
     (b) A bridge that crosses the Thames in south-west London.

9   (a) West Ham United, 1958-74.
     (b) Actor who played James Bond in films between 1973 and 1985.

10   (a) Sheffield Wednesday, 1984-94.
     (b) Brewery established in Burton-on-Trent in the mid-18th century.

1966, WEMBLEY

Sir Geoff Hurst and England win the World Cup

Photo courtesy of The Times newspaper

1   Which was the only one of England's four goals against West Germany in the 1966 World Cup final that Hurst did not score – first, second, third or fourth?

2   What was the nationality of Gottfried Dienst, who refereed the 1966 final?

3   Who were the only other team that Hurst scored against at the 1966 World Cup?

4   Hurst was the only player to have scored a hat-trick in a World Cup final until which Frenchman did so in 2022?

5   After leaving West Ham United in 1972 for which club did Hurst play for three seasons in the top flight?

6   Which London club did Hurst manage from 1979 to 1981?

7   Two members of England's World Cup-winning team have been knighted – Hurst and which other player?

PRIME MINISTER'S QUESTION TIME

Identify the players who share a surname with a British Prime Minister

1   Winger who made a record 857 appearances for Liverpool and who waited 11 years between his second cap in 1966 and his third in 1977.

2   Played left back for England in the 1966 World Cup final having begun his career with Huddersfield Town, a team based in the Yorkshire town that was the birthplace of the Prime Minister who is his namesake.

3   Manchester City and Wimbledon defender who, as a City player in 2006, was banned for eight matches by the FA for elbowing Portsmouth's Pedro Mendes.

4   Forward, nicknamed Bomber, who played a record 717 times for West Bromwich Albion and was the top flight's leading scorer in the 1970-71 season with 28 goals.

5   A Stoke City winger who won eight England caps in the 1980s, and whose son played for Arsenal and Liverpool.

6   A Scottish midfielder who played for Coventry City, was an unused substitute for Aston Villa in the 1982 European Cup final and scored a hat-trick of penalties for Sheffield Wednesday in a League Cup match against Luton Town in 1984.

7   Blond-haired centre back who began his career at Blackburn Rovers and then spent eight years at Manchester United.

8   Known as Inchy because of his short stature, this 5ft 6in striker won the League title with Everton in 1985 and 1987 and later played for Manchester City, whose manager was his former Everton team-mate Peter Reid.

9   Wales forward who helped Nottingham Forest gain promotion to the Premier League in 2022 and avoid relegation a year later.

10   Known as 'the King' at Manchester United, this Scottish forward also had two spells with Manchester City.

TREATMENT ROOM

Questions relating to notable injuries

1   Everton goalkeeper Richard Wright was injured in the warm-up ahead of their match against Chelsea in 2006 because he tripped over what?

2   Which player scored Arsenal's winning goal in the 1993 League Cup final against Sheffield Wednesday but, in the post-match celebrations, broke his arm when his team-mate Tony Adams attempted to pick him up but dropped him?

3   In 1970 how did Brentford goalkeeper Chic Brodie suffer a knee injury that ultimately ended his career?

4   Which Leeds United and England midfielder exacerbated his Achilles tendon injury when his young daughter rode her tricycle into him in 1999?

5   In 1993 which Chelsea goalkeeper was sidelined by an injury sustained when a bottle of salad cream fell on his foot?

6   How did Manchester United goalkeeper Alex Stepney dislocate his jaw during a match against Birmingham City in 1975?

7   Carlos Alcaraz injured himself when performing a knee-slide celebration after scoring the winning goal for which club against Leicester City in 2023?

8   How did West Ham United goalkeeper Roy Carroll injure his knee in training in 2005?

9   Barnsley defender Darren Barnard suffered an injury when he slipped over what in his house in 1999?

10   Which goalkeeper, who won 53 England caps, pulled a muscle when reaching for his television remote control?

TEST YOUR GEOGRAPHY

Identify the nearest English League club to the following landmarks

1   Angel of the North

2   Buckingham Palace

3   Stonehenge

4   Mount Snowdon

5   Leeds Castle

6   The Iron Bridge

7   Alton Towers

8   Cheddar Gorge

9   Scafell Pike

10   The Eden Project

11   Battle of Hastings site

12   Scotland

ROUND 20

WHAT'S THE "SCORE"?

Questions relating to the number 20

1 Which club has won a record 20 English League titles?

2 The Premier League has featured 20 clubs in every season since which year?

3 Which Manchester United and Liverpool players with the first name Diogo were wearing No 20 in 2020?

4 Which club won their 20th major trophy in 2020?

5 Who did England's women beat 20-0 a few months before becoming European champions?

6 Which Midlands club won their only League title in 1920?

7 Which striker, in February 2023, became the first to appear in the League for 20 different clubs when he made his debut for Hartlepool United?

8 Which team scored 20 goals without reply over three Premier League games either side of the 2010 summer close season (8-0 at home to Wigan Athletic; 6-0 at home to West Bromwich Albion; 6-0 away to Wigan)?

9 Who played his last match for Leeds United in 1973, 20 years and three days after his debut for that club?

10 Which Dutch club did Englishman Steve McClaren lead to a League title in 2010?

SEEING DOUBLE

Identify these pairings who played together

1   They were "soundalike" strikers who played for Crystal Palace in the 1990 FA Cup final.

2   Andy Gray and Ray Graydon were attacking team-mates at which top-flight club in the 1970s?

3   For a year and a half, two forwards named Bent were Charlton Athletic colleagues in the Premier League. What are their first names?

4   The Ameobi brothers – Shola and Sammy – played up front together for which club?

5   A Tottenham Hotspur duo with rhyming surnames appeared in the 1987 FA Cup final – Glenn Hoddle and which other player?

6   Paul Jewell and Mike Newell were strike partners with which club in the mid-1980s?

7   Stephen Hunt and his brother Noel Hunt were forwards with which club in the 2008-09 season?

8   Which two unrelated attacking players named Cole were together at West Ham United in the 2013-14 season?

9   Brian Stein scored twice in Luton Town's 3-2 win over Arsenal in the 1988 League Cup final but what was the name of his brother, team-mate and fellow forward who appeared as a substitute in that match?

10 Jamille Matt and Matt Stevens scored a combined 42 League goals to help which Cotswolds club to promotion to the third tier in the 2021-22 season?

FOUNDER MEMBERS

Name the 11 founding Football League clubs who are still active by identifying their current ground *(N.B. Accrington, the twelfth original member, folded in 1896)*

BIG FISH IN A SMALL POND

Players who were big stars in their own country

1 Manchester United and Arsenal midfielder Henrikh Mkhitaryan played for which country?

2 Which Togo striker appeared for Arsenal, Tottenham Hotspur and Manchester City?

3 Ali Al-Habsi played in which position for Bolton Wanderers and Wigan Athletic in the Premier League and for Oman?

4 Which Trinidad and Tobago forward was the Premier League's joint top scorer in 1998-99?

5 Victor Wanyama, who played in midfield for Southampton and Tottenham Hotspur, represented which east African country?

6 Which Arsenal player won 80 caps for Belarus?

7 George Weah, winner of the Ballon D'Or in 1995, played for which west African nation?

8 Which Gabon forward has played for Arsenal and Chelsea?

9 Mbwana Samatta, who scored for Aston Villa in the 2020 League Cup final, plays for which east African nation?

10 Neil Etheridge, ever-present in goal for Cardiff City in the 2018-19 Premier League season, represented which Asian nation?

THE BIG SCREEN

Films with a football theme

1 In what 2002 film – which refers to the free kick technique of an England captain – does Jess Bhamra, the daughter of Punjabi Sikhs, play football against the wishes of her parents?

2 Fever Pitch is based around which club's dramatic League title victory in 1989?

3 What 2009 film, directed by Ken Loach, features a postman who takes advice from Eric Cantona on how to overcome his problems?

4 Escape to Victory, in which Allied prisoners take on a German team, has a cast that includes a host of real players from which club?

5 The Scottish pop singer Clare Grogan appeared in which 1980 film about a girl who forces her way into the school football team?

6 The film Sixty Six is about a boy whose bar mitzvah takes place on the same day as which famous match?

7 Lock, Stock and Two Smoking Barrels features which former Wimbledon midfielder?

8 Which 2009 film focused on Brian Clough's brief spell as Leeds United manager?

9 The Game of their Lives was a 2005 film that followed the story of which nation's victory over England at the 1950 World Cup?

10 Which 1939 film was set at Arsenal's home of Highbury?

MATCH ABANDONED

Games that were called off early

1   Who scored six goals as Manchester City took a 6-2 lead against Luton Town in the FA Cup in 1961, only to have those goals struck from the record books because heavy rain forced the game to be abandoned with 21 minutes left?

2   England lost a restaged match against Czechoslovakia in Bratislava in October 1975 but what had caused the match to be abandoned on the previous day after 17 minutes?

3   A floodlight failure in the 56th minute caused the abandonment of which club's first competitive match at their new stadium in 1997?

4   On the day they were doomed to an unexpected relegation from the top flight in 1974, which club's fans forced an abandonment by invading the pitch with five minutes left – as their team trailed 1-0 to Manchester City – apparently in the vain hope that the game would have to be replayed?

5   Why was the Sheffield United v West Bromwich Albion match in 2002 abandoned after 82 minutes in what became known as the Battle of Bramall Lane?

6   Who was England's manager when their match against Ireland in Dublin in 1995 was called off after 27 minutes because of crowd trouble?

7   When Sunderland's Premier League match against Fulham in 2006 was abandoned after 21 minutes what was the unlikely cause, given that it was taking place in the month of April?

8   A floodlight failure 13 seconds into the second half caused Arsenal's Premier League match away to which club to be abandoned in December 1997?

9   On England's South American tour of 1953 their match against which nation was abandoned after 36 minutes because of a waterlogged pitch?

10   The most recent abandonment in the Premier League occurred in December 2006 because of heavy rain at which ground?

SINGING FROM THE SAME SHEET (VERSE 1)

Identify the name shared by the musical artist or band who performed the song and the player/manager/club described

1. (a) Song: (I Can't Get No) Satisfaction.
   (b) Everton and Manchester City centre back who played for England at the 2018 and 2022 World Cup.

2. (a) Song: Imagine.
   (b) Northern Irishman who played for Leicester City and Celtic and also managed the latter.

3. (a) Song: Little Lies.
   (b) Club based on the Lancashire coast who were promoted to the League in 2012.

4. (a) Song: Shake It Off.
   (b) Long-time assistant manager to Brian Clough.

5. (a) Song: I'm Too Sexy.
   (b) Brazilian midfielder who won the League Cup with Manchester United in 2023.

6. (a) Song: Saving All My Love For You.
   (b) Scottish full back who played for Manchester United in the 1970s and was Arsenal's manager in the 1995 Cup Winners' Cup final defeat to Real Zaragoza.

7. (a) Song: School's Out.
   (b) Leeds United left back who played for England in the 1970 World Cup quarter-finals.

8. (a) Song: Happy.
   (b) Liverpool and Arsenal midfielder who won a record 172 caps for the England women's team.

9. (a) Song: Make It Easy On Yourself.
   (b) Nottingham Forest and Sheffield Wednesday centre back who played for England in the World Cup semi-finals in 1990.

10. (a) Song: Mary's Prayer.
    (b) Barnsley's Northern Irish manager in 1997-98, their only season in the top flight.

ROUND 27

EMOJI TIME

Identify the names of these 21st-century top-flight players from these images
(with some poetic licence!)

1

6

2

7

3

8

4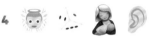

9

5 **F** ⬤

10

And now do the same to identify these League clubs...

11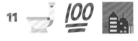

16

12

17

13

18

14

19

15

20

KEEPING UP WITH THE JONESES

Give the first name of each Jones

1   Welshman and former Luton Town manager whose brief spell in charge of Southampton in the 2022-23 season featured only eight Premier League games.

2   Liverpool's left back in the 1977 European Cup final.

3   Centre back or midfielder who spent 12 years at Manchester United from 2011.

4   Forward who won the League, FA Cup, League Cup and Inter-Cities Fairs Cup with Leeds United.

5   Winger who reached the World Cup quarter-finals in 1958 with Wales and won the double with Tottenham Hotspur in 1960-61.

6   Everton defender who managed six League clubs, including Southampton, Wolverhampton Wanderers and Sheffield Wednesday.

7   Australian goalkeeper who played for Middlesbrough when Gareth Southgate was manager.

8   Midfielder who played for Coventry City in the 1990s and won a record 164 caps for the United States.

9   Merseyside-born midfielder who made 18 League appearances for Liverpool in the 2022-23 season.

10   Assistant to Roberto Martínez when the latter managed Swansea City, Wigan Athletic, Everton and Belgium?

CHRISTMAS GREETINGS

Matches played in the festive period

1 Which teams contested the most recent English League fixture to have been played on Christmas Day (it was in the top division in 1965)?

2 Which club sacked their manager on Christmas Eve in both 1973 (Derek Dooley) and 2017 (Carlos Carvalhal)?

3 Dennis Bailey scored a hat-trick for which London club at Old Trafford in a 4-1 win over Manchester United on New Year's Day in 1992?

4 Which top-division club, fed up with starting the season poorly and only getting into their stride in the New Year, brought forward their 1992 Christmas party to the summer to get them in the right frame of mind?

5 Which "Santa" – a Paraguayan – played for Blackburn Rovers and Manchester City in the Premier League?

6 Which Scotland midfielder and Coventry City and Leeds United manager was born on Christmas Day?

7 In which decade were the last League matches played in Scotland on Christmas Day?

8 Having just left West Ham United, who became Charlton Athletic manager on Christmas Eve in 2006?

9 Which club beat Ipswich Town 10-1 on Boxing Day in 1963 yet lost 4-2 away to the same opponents just two days later?

10 Which team, managed by Howard Wilkinson, beat Manchester United in 1995 in the last League match to have been played on Christmas Eve?

GONE CLUBBING

Identify the club from the following information

1   *Year formed:* 1884. *Highest League position:* 1st in top flight in 2016.
Best FA Cup run: winners in 2021. *Most appearances:* Graham Cross, 609.

2   *Year formed:* 1868. *Highest League position:* 4th in top flight 1936 and 1947.
Best FA Cup run: runners-up in 2011. *Most appearances:* Eric Skeels, 598.

3   *Year formed:* 1895. *Highest League position:* 3rd in top flight in 1986.
Best FA Cup run: winners in 1964, 1975 and 1980. *Most appearances:* Billy
Bonds, 799.

4   *Year formed:* 1886. *Highest League position:* 4th in second tier 1932 and 1953.
Best FA Cup run: semi-finals in 1984. *Most appearances:* Kevin Hodges, 620.

5   *Year formed:* 1875. *Highest League position:* 6th in top flight in 1956.
Best FA Cup run: runners-up in 1931 and 1956. *Most appearances:* Gil Merrick
551.

6   *Year formed:* 1867. *Highest League position:* 4th in second tier in 1947. *Best FA
Cup run:* semi-finals in 1997. *Most appearances:* Dave Blakey, 659.

7   *Year formed:* 1881. *Highest League position:* 2nd in top flight in 1983.
Best FA Cup run: runners-up in 1984 and 2019. *Most appearances:* Luther
Blissett, 503.

8   *Year formed:* 1881. *Highest League position:* 22nd in top flight in 1963.
Best FA Cup run: semi-finals in 1978. *Most appearances:* Peter Allen, 490.

9   *Year formed:* 1878. *Highest League position:* 1st in top flight in 1962.
Best FA Cup run: winners in 1978. *Most appearances:* Mick Mills, 741.

10   *Year formed:* 1883. *Highest League position:* 6th in top flight in 1970.
Best FA Cup run: winners in 1987. *Most appearances:* Steve Ogrizovic, 601.

1998, SAINT-ETIENNE

David Beckham's red card

Photo courtesy of The Times newspaper

1 Beckham was sent off for kicking which Argentina player?

2 Which teenager had scored for England earlier in the match?

3 Which two England players failed from the spot in the penalty shoot-out in this match?

4 Kim Milton Nielsen, the Danish referee who dismissed Beckham, gave a second yellow card to which Manchester United player for clapping him sarcastically in 2005?

5 For which club was Beckham a player when he won his 100th England cap in 2008?

6 Nelson Vivas, the Argentina No14 in the picture, joined which Premier League club shortly after the World Cup?

7 Against which country was Beckham sent off in a World Cup qualifier in 2005?

EURO HEROES

Match the English club to the European final in which they played

1	1981 Uefa Cup final	**A**	Newcastle United
2	1963 Cup Winners' Cup final	**B**	West Ham United
3	2006 Champions League final	**C**	Manchester City
4	1969 Fairs Cup final	**D**	Fulham
5	1982 European Cup final	**E**	Everton
6	2023 Europa Conference League final	**F**	Arsenal
7	1970 Cup Winners' Cup final	**G**	Middlesbrough
8	2010 Europa League final	**H**	Liverpool
9	1985 Cup Winners' Cup final	**I**	Nottingham Forest
10	1980 European Cup final	**J**	Ipswich Town
11	1991 Cup Winners' Cup	**K**	Chelsea
12	1975 European Cup final	**L**	Aston Villa
13	1966 Cup Winners' Cup final	**M**	Manchester United
14	2006 Uefa Cup final	**N**	Leeds United
15	1971 Cup Winners' Cup final	**O**	Tottenham Hotspur

FOOD FOR THOUGHT

Questions which are "food-related"

1 Which Rice captained a Ham to victory in the Europa Conference League final in 2023?

2 David Peach scored for which club in their defeat to Nottingham Forest in the 1979 League Cup final?

3 What did Sutton United's reserve goalkeeper Wayne Shaw eat while on the substitutes' bench during an FA Cup match at home to Arsenal?

4 Which England midfielder had Mars Bars thrown at him by opposition fans because they were a favourite snack of his?

5 Which former Sunderland, Liverpool and Newcastle United player co-presented On the Ball with Gabby Logan on ITV?

6 Which England goalkeeper missed the World Cup quarter-final match against West Germany in 1970 because of food poisoning?

7 What did Arsenal's Cesc Fàbregas throw at Manchester United manager Sir Alex Ferguson after a match at Old Trafford in 2004?

8 Which South African defender moved from Bolton Wanderers to Charlton Athletic in 2000?

9 What vegetable was thrown at Aston Villa manager Steve Bruce during a match against Preston North End in 2018?

10 Which team were weakened by a bout of food poisoning – said to be from a lasagne – on the last day of the 2005-06 season (their defeat allowed Arsenal to qualify for the Champions League instead of them)?

CAREERING AROUND

Identify these players from their clubs and the year of their first appearance

1 West Ham United 1999 - Chelsea 2003 - Liverpool 2010 - Lille *(loan)* 2011 - West Ham United 2013 - Aston Villa 2014 - Coventry City 2015 *(initially on loan)* - Tampa Bay Rowdies 2016

2 Manchester United 1956 - Preston North End 1974 - Waterford 1976 - Newcastle KB United 1978 - Perth Azzurri 1980 - Blacktown City 1980

3 Burnley *(loan from Aston Villa)* 2004 - Aston Villa 2005 - Sheffield United *(loan)* 2007 - Bolton Wanderers 2008 - Chelsea 2012 - Crystal Palace 2019 - Bournemouth 2021

4 Wimbledon 1985 - Grebbestads IF *(loan)* 1985 - Chelsea 1990 - Leicester City 2001 - Millwall 2002 - Southampton 2005 - Coventry City 2006

5 Scunthorpe United 1966 - Liverpool 1968 - Tottenham Hotspur 1981

6 Gillingham 1982 - Millwall 1987 - Aston Villa 1990 - Celtic 1991 - Chelsea 1992 - Marseille 1994 - Nancy 1996 - Red Star 93 2000

7 Leeds United 1984 - Oldham Athletic 1986 - Manchester United 1990 - Wolverhampton Wanderers 2002

8 Tottenham Hotspur 1992 - Middlesbrough 1995 - Everton 1996 - Liverpool 2000 - Leeds United 2002 - Nottingham Forest *(loan)* 2004 - Hull City 2004

9 Leeds United 2007 - Aston Villa 2009 - Leeds United *(loan)* 2012 - Manchester City 2015 - Everton 2019

10 Charlton Athletic 1997 - Norwich City *(loan)* 2000 - Chelsea 2004 - Newcastle United 2005 - West Ham United 2007 - Tottenham Hotspur 2011 - Fulham 2013

PASSPORT CONTROL

Identify these players from their personal details

1 Born Leicester, November 30th 1960 - 5ft 10in - striker

2 Born Preston, April 5th 1922 - 5ft 8in - winger

3 Born Macclesfield, January 30th 1981 - 6ft 7in - striker

4 Born Jersey, October 17th 1968 - 5ft 10in - left back

5 Born Cannock, January 22nd 1971 - 6ft 2in - striker

6 Born Aberdeen, February 24th 1994 - 5ft 4in - winger

7 Born Dudley, October 1st 1936 - 5ft 11in - midfielder

8 Born Guernsey, October 14th 1968 - 6ft 1in - forward

9 Born Oxford, July 24th 1966 - 6ft 1in - centre back

10 Born Plymouth, April 19th 1954 - 5ft 10in - striker

11 Born St Austell, August 11th 1966 - 6ft 2in - goalkeeper

12 Born Newcastle, August 13th 1970 - 6ft 0in - striker

GETTING SHIRTY

Questions relating to shirt numbers

1 George Best, David Beckham and Cristiano Ronaldo all wore which shirt number for Manchester United in European Cup or Champions League finals?

2 What number did Ossie Ardiles wear when playing for Argentina at the 1982 World Cup?

3 When Liverpool won the League in 1990 their shirt numbers totalled 66 (1 to 11). Which player wore No 66 when they next became champions in 2020?

4 In which season were squad numbers first worn on shirts in the Premier League, a campaign in which Manchester United recorded the League and FA Cup double?

5 Despite being a striker, who wore the No 3 shirt for Ghana at the 2010 World Cup and for Sunderland in the 2011-12 season?

6 When Aston Villa played Liverpool in the League Cup in December 2019 what number did Liverpool's Tom Hill wear – the highest that is allowed in English football?

7 Which number did Khalid Boulahrouz wear for Chelsea in the 2006-07 season even though he was a defender?

8 Which shirt number did Jackie Milburn and Alan Shearer wear as Newcastle United players?

9 In which decade did the FA Cup final first feature numbered shirts?

10 Which player wore No 87 on his Premier League debut for Arsenal in January 2019 but has since taken on the No 7 shirt for the Gunners?

ON THE SPOT

Questions relating to penalties

1   Which goalkeeper, playing for Wimbledon against Liverpool in 1988, became the first to save a penalty in an FA Cup final?

2   Which Arsenal player tried to pass to his team-mate Thierry Henry from a penalty against Manchester City in 2005?

3   The only player in League history to have scored four penalties in one League game is Cameron Brannagan, who did so for which club in a 7-2 win away Gillingham in 2022?

4   Chelsea's top League scorer in 2020-21 did not manage a single goal from open play – his seven goals all came from penalties. Name him.

5   Francis Lee converted 13 penalties in the League in 1971-72, the most by any player in one season. For which club was he playing?

6   Which Nigerian forward, who appeared for Newcastle United and Birmingham City, took four penalties in the Premier League – two with each feet?

7   Which player – and captain – failed from the spot during England's 2-1 defeat to the United States in the Women's World Cup semi-finals in 2019?

8   Which Manchester United goalkeeper, playing in a 6-0 defeat away to Ipswich Town in 1980, saved a spot-kick by Frans Thijssen and also kept out both attempts of a twice-taken penalty by Kevin Beattie?

9   Nathan Dyer was playing for which club in the 2013 League Cup final when, having already scored twice, he was angered by the refusal of his team-mates to let him attempt to complete a hat-trick by taking a penalty?

10   Marcus Rashford, Bukayo Saka and which other player failed with their penalties in the shoot-out when England lost the Euro 2020 final to Italy?

SET YOUR SAT-NAV

Match the postcode to the League ground

1	N5 1BU	**A**	Elland Road (home of Leeds United)
2	WV1 4QR	**B**	The City Ground (Nottingham Forest)
3	M16 0RA	**C**	Stadium of Light (Sunderland)
4	NG2 5FJ	**D**	Ashton Gate (Bristol City)
5	BS3 2LQ	**E**	Molineux (Wolverhampton Wanderers)
6	SE25 6PU	**F**	Portman Road (Ipswich Town)
7	PR1 6RU	**G**	Selhurst Park (Crystal Palace)
8	B6 6HE	**H**	Villa Park (Birmingham City)
9	NR1 1JE	**I**	Old Trafford (Manchester United)
10	L4 0TH	**J**	Carrow Road (Norwich City)
11	SR5 1SU	**K**	Anfield (Liverpool)
12	TW8 0RU	**L**	Deepdale (Preston North End)
13	IP1 2DA	**M**	Emirates Stadium (Arsenal)
14	EX4 6PU	**N**	Brentford Community Stadium (Brentford)
15	LS11 0ES	**O**	St James Park (Exeter City)

ROUND 39

WAY IN

Identify the ground from the gates, turnstiles or walkway

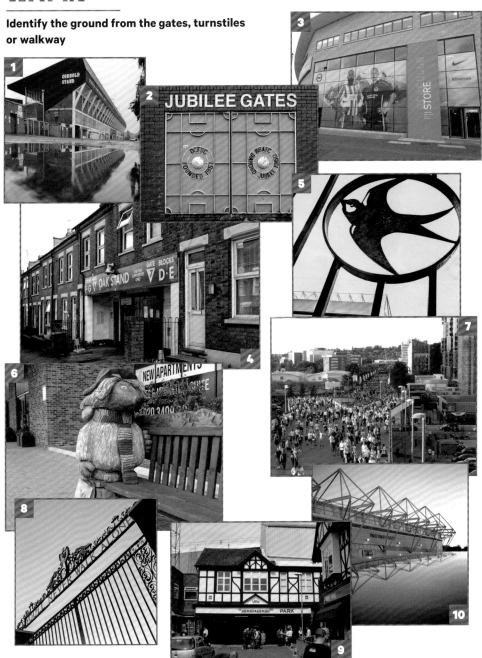

Photos courtesy of footballstadiumphotography.co.uk and iansapps.co.uk

FRAUGHT FINALE

The end-of-season play-offs

1 Who scored West Ham United's winner in their 1-0 victory over Preston North End in the 2005 second-tier play-off final and also the only goal as Queens Park Rangers defeated Derby County in the 2014 second-tier final?

2 Which is the only club to have won a shoot-out in a play-off final after a 0-0 draw – and they have done it three times (their managers were Peter Jackson, Simon Grayson and David Wagner).

3 Which team beat Sunderland on penalties after a 4-4 draw in the second-tier final in 1998 and defeated them again with a winner in the fourth minute of stoppage time in the third-tier final in 2019?

4 Which club has won a record six play-off finals, two more than any other team?

5 Only one team has overcome a first-leg deficit of more than two goals to win a two-legged play-off tie – and they did so by recovering from as much as 4-0 down against Peterborough United in 2023. Name the team.

6 Which defender, on loan from Chelsea, scored an own goal in the second-tier final in 2022 as Nottingham Forest beat Huddersfield Town 1-0?

7 Which club has won four second-tier finals, two more than any other team?

8 In the first two seasons of the play-offs the lowest-placed team from the division above were involved: Charlton Athletic maintained their top-flight status in 1987 but which other London club were relegated from the top division via the play-offs in 1988?

9 Which team ended a 16-year wait to return to the top flight by beating Norwich City in the 2002 play-off final having lost in the semi-finals in each of the previous three seasons?

10 Which East London team are the only side to have scored six goals in a play-off game, beating Morecambe 6-0 in 2010?

CREATURE CURIOSITIES

Delve into the animal kingdom to find the answers

1   What nickname did Nat Lofthouse earn with a battling performance for England away to Austria in 1952?

2   Razvan Rat, the Romanian left back, played for which London club in the Premier League in the 2013-14 season?

3   Who scored all seven goals for Arsenal in their 7-1 win away to Aston Villa in December 1935?

4   Which club were captained by the aptly named Dutchman John de Wolf from 1994 to 1996?

5   Which Chelsea and England goalkeeper was known as The Cat?

6   Christian Pander scored the winning goal for which country against England at Wembley in 2007?

7   Who was banned from football for eight years from 1964 because of his involvement in a betting scandal?

8   What was the nickname of the Queens Park Rangers and West Ham United midfielder Martin Allen?

9   Who was the long-haired English centre back who was a regular for Newcastle United as they finished second in the top flight two years in a row in the mid-1990s?

10   At which club was the American Bruce Buck the chairman?

ONE-CAP WONDERS

Match the England one-cap wonder from his initials, club, year of the match and opponents

1 **TS** - Liverpool defender - 1971 - Wales

2 **CS** - Blackburn Rovers forward - 1997 - Cameroon

3 **SP** - Tottenham Hotspur defender/midfielder - 1982 - Iceland

4 **CK** - Liverpool goalkeeper - 2006 - Greece

5 **MP** - Manchester United midfielder - 1989 - Italy

6 **RS** - Stoke City defender - 2012 - Sweden

7 **BL** - Aston Villa forward - 1975 - Wales

8 **DN** - Preston North End forward - 2007 - Andorra

9 **CG** - Derby County forward - 1976 - Republic of Ireland

10 **JB** - Manchester City midfielder - 2007 - Spain

11 **KD** - Bolton Wanderers striker - 2010 - Montenegro

12 **DW** - Southampton striker - 1986 - Egypt

13 **JH** - Chelsea midfielder - 1967 - Spain

14 **NS** - Aston Villa goalkeeper - 1983 - Australia

15 **BM** - Arsenal midfielder - 1988 - Saudi Arabia

CITY SLICKERS

Identify these current League clubs with City in their name

1 B _ _ M _ _ _ _ _ M CITY

2 _ _ _ _ H _ S _ _ _ CITY

3 _ _ R W _ _ _ CITY

4 _ _ I _ E _ _ E _ CITY

5 _ _ _ K _ CITY

6 B _ _ _ _ O _ CITY

7 _ W _ _ S _ _ CITY

8 _ _ V _ _ _ _ Y CITY

9 _ U _ _ CITY

10 _ _ _ _ _ F F CITY

11 _ _ _ D _ _ _ D CITY

12 L _ _ _ _ L _ CITY

13 _ X _ _ _ _ CITY

14 _ A _ _ O _ _ CITY

COMING OFF THE BENCH

Questions relating to substitutions

1   Which England striker did Graham Taylor controversially take off after about an hour of the decisive group match against Sweden at Euro 1992?

2   Who scored for Manchester United as early as the 11th minute of the 1999 FA Cup final – as a substitute?

3   Who were England's opponents when they did not use any substitutes in their Euro 1996 semi-final even though the match went to extra time?

4   The first substitute to score a hat-trick in a top-division game was Frank McAvennie against Nottingham Forest in May 1992. For which team was he playing?

5   Late during a match against Middlesbrough in 2005, Manchester City moved their goalkeeper forward as an outfield player and brought on the reserve goalkeeper as a substitute. Who was the goalkeeper who became a striker for a few minutes?

6   Which Charlton Athletic midfielder became the first player to appear as a substitute in a League game in 1965?

7   In terms of substitutions, what was unusual about the match between Manchester United and Fulham in March 2003?

8   Which Everton striker made a top-flight-record 29 substitute appearances in the 2004-05 season?

9   Which manager surprisingly started Alan Shearer on the bench in a match against Sunderland in 1999 in what proved his last game as Newcastle United manager?

10   Which Northern Irish winger – once of Manchester United – was sent off on arriving as a substitute for Sheffield United against Reading in 2007 before the restart of play (he pushed Reading's Stephen Hunt).

GOING TO THE MATCH

Identify the stadium reached at the end of this journey based on the starting point, distance travelled and the main roads taken

1   Start: Tottenham Hotspur Stadium.
    6 miles. High Road, Seven Sisters Road

2   Start: City Ground (Nottingham Forest).
    17 miles. A52

3   Start: Portman Road (Ipswich Town).
    45 miles. A140

4   Start: Selhurst Park (Crystal Palace).
    46 miles. A23, M23

5   Start: Deepdale (Preston North End).
    17 miles. M55

6   Start: St James Park (Exeter City).
    46 miles. A38

7   Start: Molineux (Wolverhampton Wanderers).
    31 miles. M54, A5

8   Start: Riverside Stadium (Middlesbrough).
    43 miles. A19, A184

9   Start: Brisbane Road (Leyton Orient).
    54 miles. M11

10 Start: Elland Road (Leeds United).
    38 miles. M62, A646

11 Start: Brunton Park (Carlisle United).
    70 miles. M6, A683

12 Start: St Mary's Stadium (Southampton).
    45 miles. M3, A33

2022, QATAR

Lionel Messi and Argentina win the World Cup

Photo courtesy of The Times newspaper

1 Lionel Messi scored twice against which Premier League goalkeeper in the 2022 World Cup final?

2 After Messi scored Argentina's opening goal of the World Cup semi-final against Croatia in 2022 which Manchester City player added the team's other two goals?

3 Which Aston Villa goalkeeper helped Argentina win the shoot-out in the final to allow Messi to lift the trophy as captain?

4 How many appearances has Messi made against England?

5 An Argentina team led by Messi won the 2022 Finalissima – a match featuring the champions of South America and Europe and played at which venue?

6 Against which Premier League club did Messi score four times in a Champions League match in 2010?

7 Messi scored direct from a free kick against which Premier League team in the Champions League semi-finals in 2019?

OWN GOALS

Players who scored against their own goalkeeper

1   Which young centre forward scored a hat-trick and an own goal in the same match when playing for Chelsea against Wolverhampton Wanderers in September 2019?

2   Which club are responsible for both cases of a team scoring three own goals in one top-flight match, doing so against Charlton Athletic in 2003 and against Southampton in 2014?

3   In March 1976 which Aston Villa defender scored twice for his own team and twice for opponents Leicester City in a 2-2 draw?

4   Graham Roberts was playing for which club when he scored two own goals in a surprising 4-1 home defeat to Burnley in the League Cup in January 1983?

5   Which Midlands club beat Den Haag 4-0 in a Uefa Cup match in 1971 helped by three own goals?

6   For which club was Kevin Bond playing when he scored an own goal and a penalty in a top-division match against Stoke City in March 1980 – and then did exactly the same seven days later against West Bromwich Albion?

7   Fankaty Dabo was playing for which team against Oxford United in 2019 when he scored two own goals (he was still at that club in 2023 when he missed the decisive kick in a penalty shoot-out defeat in a play-off final)?

8   Queens Park Rangers advanced from the League Cup semi-finals in 1985-86 with a 3-2 aggregate win after a 2-2 away draw in the second leg in which Ronnie Whelan and Gary Gillespie – two of their opponents – scored own goals. Who were the opposing team?

9   Which team, managed by David Pleat, benefitted from an own goal in four consecutive games in 1979?

10   Which defender, who played for Manchester City in the 1955 and 1956 FA Cup finals, scored 12 own goals in his career, the most by any player for League clubs in all competitions (ten for City, two for Crewe Alexandra)?

HAT-TRICK HEROES

Players who scored three or more goals in one match

1   Which future Liverpool player scored in the 13th, 14th and 16th minutes for Southampton against Aston Villa in May 2015?

2   Which player scored the most recent top-flight double hat-trick – six goals for West Ham United against Sunderland in October 1968 – two years after a more famous hat-trick for England?

3   Who, either side of a brief spell at AC Milan in 1961, scored hat-tricks in consecutive appearances in English football – four goals in his last match for Chelsea and then three in his first game for Tottenham Hotspur?

4   It was dubbed the Matthews Final, after Blackpool's Sir Stanley Matthews, but which of his team-mates scored what remains the last hat-trick in an FA Cup final as Bolton Wanderers were beaten 4-3 in 1953?

5   Which Arsenal player scored in three different stoppage times in their 7-5 away win against Reading in the League Cup in October 2012: in the first half, in the second half and at the end of the second period of extra time?

6   Which player, active between the two world wars, has scored a record 37 League hat-tricks, 11 more than any other player?

7   When David Speedie and Bernie Slaven hit hat-tricks in the same top-flight match in October 1988 for which clubs were they playing?

8   Who scored a hat-trick for Arsenal against Newcastle United in December 1976 four months after leaving the North East club?

9   James Hayter scored a hat-trick in two minutes and 22 seconds for which club against Wrexham in February 2004?

10   Which 16-year-old and future England player scored a hat-trick for Birmingham City against Bolton Wanderers in February 1971?

ROUND 49

GLOBAL VISION

Identify the year and host nation of these World Cups by the name of that country's leader at the time and England's progress in that tournament.

1 (a) Leader: Angela Merkel.
(b) England: lost to Portugal in quarter-finals

2 (a) Leader: Leopoldo Calvo-Sotelo.
(b) England: eliminated in second group stage

3 (a) Leader: Jacques Chirac.
(b) England: lost to Argentina in round-of-16

4 (a) Leader: Vladimir Putin.
(b) England: lost to Croatia in semi-finals

5 (a) Leader: Jacob Zuma.
(b) England: lost to Germany in round-of-16

6 (a) Leader: Gustavo Díaz Ordaz.
(b) England: lost to West Germany in quarter-finals

7 (a) Leader: Giulio Andreotti.
(b) England: lost to West Germany in semi-finals

8 (a) Leader: Dilma Rousseff.
(b) England: eliminated in group stage

9 (a) Leader: Tage Erlander.
(b) England: lost to Soviet Union in group stage play-off

10 (a) Leader: Sheikh Tamim bin Hamad al Thani.
(b) England: lost to France in quarter-finals

11 (a) Leader: Miguel de la Madrid.
(b) England: lost to Argentina in quarter-finals

12 (a) Leader: Jorge Alessandri.
(b) England: lost to Brazil in quarter-finals

I'M A CELEBRITY...

Identify these stars of stage, screen, sport and politics

ROUND 51
PUT YOUR SHIRT ON IT

Identify the club from their shirt sponsors

1   Candy - Hitachi - Crown Paints

2   Holsten - HP - Mansion

3   AVCO - BAC Windows - Dr Martens

4   Amiga - Coors - Autoglass

5   Colman's - Aviva - Lotus

6   NEC - one2one - Chang

7   Fly Virgin - TDK - Churchill

8   Brother - Eidos - Thomas Cook

9   Triton Showers - Auto Windscreens - Phones4u

10   Top Man - Thistle Hotels - Packard Bell

11   Draper Tools - Sanderson - Friends Provident

12   Talbot - Peugeot - City Link

HAPPY FAMILIES (PART 2)

Questions relating to footballing families

1   What is the surname of the father and son both with a first name George who played for England?

2   Which club won the FA Cup finals of 1977 (against Liverpool) and 1999 (against Newcastle United) and fielded a pair of brothers in the starting line-up each time?

3   Which Englishman managed Wales but has a son who played for Scotland?

4   Bill Dodgin Snr and his son Bill Dodgin Jnr managed the same two west London clubs. Name them.

5   A player who appeared for Hull City in the 2014 FA Cup final has a sister who won the Women's FA Cup with Charlton Athletic, Birmingham City and Chelsea. Who are these siblings?

6   Nathaniel Chalobah, who played for England in 2018, and his brother Trevoh Chalobah, the Chelsea defender, were both born in which African country?

7   Alan Ball Snr, who managed three League clubs, had the full name James Alan Ball. What was the full name of his son, Alan Ball Jnr, who won the World Cup as a player with England in 1966?

8   Which teams were facing each other at the 2010 and 2014 World Cups when Kevin-Prince Boateng and his half-brother Jérôme Boateng were in opposition?

9   Ian Bowyer, the player-manager, appeared alongside his son Gary Bowyer in two League matches in 1990 for which club?

10 When Middlesbrough finished top of the second tier in 1973-74 while Preston North End were relegated from that division who were the two brothers managing those clubs?

IN THE DOCK

Clubs who suffered points deductions

1 Which club was League champions in 1990-91 despite suffering a two-point penalty imposed for their players fighting in a match?

2 Who were the opponents in the above match – they had one point taken away for their role in the fight (it remains the only top-flight game in which player misbehaviour led to a points deduction)?

3 Who were deducted three points – which ultimately led to their relegation from the top flight – for failing to turn up for a match against Blackburn Rovers in 1996-97 (they were hit by illness and injury)?

4 Which club was promoted to the third tier in 2000-01 despite being docked nine points for breaking financial rules?

5 Who reached the FA Cup final in 2010 in a season when they were relegated after being deducted nine points for entering administration (they would have been relegated anyway)?

6 Who finished bottom of the third and fourth tiers in 2007-08 and 2008-09 having been given a points penalty of 10 and 30 respectively in those seasons?

7 Which club was denied automatic promotion from the third tier in 2007-08 because they had lost 15 points for breaking rules relating to exiting administration?

8 Which Yorkshire club are alone in having been given a points penalty on four different occasions?

9 Who was Derby County's manager when they were relegated from the second tier in 2022 because of a 21-point deduction for entering administration and breaching accounting rules?

10 Who were the only top-flight club to be docked points between 1888, when the League was formed, and 1990 – they lost two points for fielding an ineligible player in 1890-91, a decade in which they won three League titles?

BEYOND THE BOUNDARY

Football and cricket

1   Which World Cup winner with England in 1966 played one first-class match for Essex – in which he did not score a run or take a wicket?

2   Who appeared for England in the 1985 Ashes series and also played in Sir Bobby Charlton's last match for Manchester United in 1973?

3   Chris Balderstone played a League match for which club in the middle of scoring a century for Leicestershire in September 1975 (the innings lasted two days)?

4   Which medium-pace bowler helped England win the women's cricket World Cup in 1993 and, as a centre back, played at the football World Cup two years later?

5   For which League club did Ian Botham play?

6   Until their move to a new home in 1994, which club tended to wait a few weeks to play their first home match of the season because they shared their ground with the local county cricket club?

7   Which former Rangers goalkeeper played football and cricket for Scotland?

8   Which two grounds have staged Test cricket and the FA Cup final?

9   Who kept goal for West Ham United when they won the 1964 FA Cup final and also that year, as a medium-pacer with Worcestershire, topped the first-class bowling averages?

10   Which England squad member at the 1950 World Cup also appeared in 23 cricket Tests?

DOWN ON THE FARM

Questions with a "farming" connection

1 John Farmer was goalkeeper for which Midlands club when they lost 4-0 in their first ever European away game against Kaiserslautern in 1972?

2 Gary Lineker considers which footballer to be the GOAT (greatest of all time)?

3 Sutton United play at ------ Green Lane. Fill in the gap.

4 Which Bull was the player-coach of the Bulls – Hereford United – in the 2000-01 season?

5 Which Geoff, who played in the Premier League for Birmingham City, West Bromwich Albion and Sheffield United, might have enjoyed a sugar lump or a carrot?

6 Ernie Shepherd managed which Essex club in the late 1960s?

7 Alex Herd and his son David Herd started a League game together for which club in May 1951?

8 Who are the Tractor Boys?

9 Which Celtic midfielder played for Scotland at the 1974 World Cup shortly before moving to Chelsea?

10 Sam Field played for which club during their Premier League relegation seasons of 2017-18 and 2020-21?

ROUND 56
I'M IN CHARGE

Questions relating to referees

1   At the 2006 World Cup, which English referee failed to send off Croatia's Josip Simunic when booking him for a second time in the match against Australia (he eventually dismissed that player after showing him a third yellow card)?

2   Which Sheffield Wednesday player pushed referee Paul Alcock to the ground during a Premier League match against Arsenal in September 1998 after the official had shown him a red card?

3   In the space of eight weeks in 2016 which referee oversaw the finals of the FA Cup, Champions League and European Championship?

4   In the match between Brazil and Sweden at the 1978 World Cup which referee blew the full-time whistle immediately after a corner had been taken, which meant that what had appeared to be the winning goal scored by Brazil moments later did not count?

5   Which Premier League referee stepped out of the crowd at a women's match between Arsenal and Reading in 2015 – refereed by his wife – to replace the injured assistant referee?

6   In the 2010 World Cup final which Everton player, who was appearing for the Netherlands against Spain, did Howard Webb send off?

7   Who, in his 2006 autobiography, said he delayed the final whistle of his last match as a referee – a fixture at Anfield – because he wanted to wait until the ball was at the Kop end?

8   Who awarded The Netherlands a penalty one minute into the 1974 World Cup final against hosts West Germany?

9   Which Italian referee oversaw the 1999 Champions League final between Manchester United and Bayern Munich?

10   Which aptly named Surrey village was the home of referee Ray Lewis for most of his career?

ROUND 57

UNITED NATIONS' FLAG DAYS

Identify the six Premier League winning teams below and give the year they won the Premier League along with all the players' names

1

2

3

4

5

6

COLOUR-CODED

Players with "colourful" surnames

1 Aston Villa striker who received two PFA awards in 1977 – Players' Player of the Year and Young Player of the Year.

2 Scot who won the double with Tottenham Hotspur in 1960-61 and was killed by lightning in 1964.

3 West Ham United goalkeeper who played for England at the 2010 World Cup.

4 Left winger who played in League Cup finals both for Nottingham Forest (in 1992) and against them (for Luton Town in 1989).

5 Co-owner of Birmingham City and West Ham United who died in 2023.

6 Right back who was a World Cup runner-up in 2023 with the England women's team and who plays club football in Spain, the country that beat England in the final.

7 Club with whom Dennis Viollet won League titles in 1956 and 1957.

8 Arsenal, Sunderland and Sweden midfielder whose surname is the German for black.

9 Club for which Mike Salmon made 148 League appearances in the 1990s.

10 Ipswich Town and Colchester United defender who also managed the latter.

11 England left back who scored ten minutes into his Premier League debut for Tottenham Hotspur against Arsenal in 2010.

12 Manchester United defender whose surname is the French for white.

DID THAT REALLY HAPPEN?

Identify the ground where the following events occurred

1   Where Cardiff City were drawn to play away in three consecutive FA Cup third rounds from 1956 to 1958 – and won 2-1 each time.

2   Where, on matchdays, a man in a small boat waited next to a League club's ground to collect and return any footballs kicked into the river.

3   Where, in February 1972, Northern Ireland played a home European Championship qualifier against Spain.

4   Where, in October 2009, Darren Bent scored against Liverpool with a shot that deflected into the goal via a beach ball thrown from the crowd.

5   Where, in September 1972, ITV's Head of Sport Jimmy Hill, who was in the crowd, replaced an injured linesman.

6   Where, as a manager in the mid-1990s, Barry Fry urinated on the four corners of his club's pitch in an attempt to lift a curse supposedly left by travellers who had been moved to allow the ground to be built.

7   Where, in November 1968, Plymouth Argyle were beaten 1-0 via a freakish goal: a shot by the home team's George McLean was going wide until it deflected into the net off the referee Ivan Robinson.

8   Where, in July 1966, North Korea beat Italy to eliminate them from the World Cup.

9   Where, in January 1979, the home side's team-mates Derek Hales and Mike Flanagan were sent off for fighting with each other in an FA Cup match against Maidstone United.

10   Where, in September 1981, a League Cup match was abandoned when the home goalkeeper Gren Millington broke the frame of the goal by colliding with it as he made a save against Plymouth Argyle.

11   Where, in November 1997, Dean Windass received three red cards in one match for Aberdeen: the first for a second yellow card, the second for subsequent verbal dissent and the third, as he left the pitch, for removing the corner flag and throwing it to the ground.

12   Where, in June 2002, Michael Jackson appeared at a club fund-raising event and addressed the crowd.

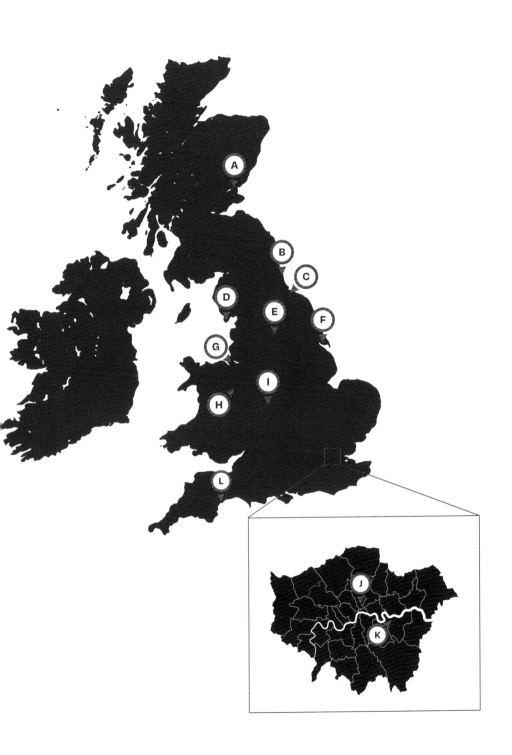

BROWNIE POINTS

Give the first name of each Brown

1   Locally born defender who made 362 appearances for Manchester United from 1998 to 2011.

2   Defender alongside Bobby Moore as West Ham United won the FA Cup and Cup Winners' Cup, and manager of Norwich City when they finished fifth in the top flight in 1987.

3   Preston North End manager who also led Scotland at the 1998 World Cup.

4   Won 82 caps for England Women and has become a television pundit.

5   Midfielder who played in the Premier League with Manchester City, Tottenham Hotspur, Fulham, Wigan Athletic and Portsmouth.

6   Scottish goalkeeper who won the double with Tottenham Hotspur in 1960-61.

7   Everton left back who scored a memorable headed own goal in the home defeat to Liverpool in 1969.

8   Bolton Wanderers full back who was assistant to manager Sam Allardyce at that club for six years and later managed Hull City in the Premier League.

9   Scottish forward who played for West Bromwich Albion between 1972 and 1983.

10   Celtic and Scotland midfielder who became Fleetwood Town manager in 2022.

ROUND 61

HY-FUN

Players with double-barrel surnames

1   England right back who helped Liverpool win the Champions League in 2019.

2   Current West Ham United midfielder who specialises at scoring direct from free kicks.

3   Premier League club for whom Cameroon forward Eric Maxim Choupo-Moting played in his late twenties in the 2017-18 campaign before winning League titles in each of the next five seasons with Paris Saint-Germain (two) and Bayern Munich (three).

4   French winger who joined Newcastle United from Nice in 2019 and is renowned for his dribbling.

5   England winger who joined Manchester United from Nottingham Forest in March 1972.

6   Chelsea winger who made his England debut in 2019 and had a spell on loan to Bayer Leverkusen.

7   Reading and West Bromwich Albion forward who scored a brilliant goal for Wales in their quarter-final victory over Belgium at Euro 2016.

8   Lotte Wubben-Moy has played as a defender for England Women and has also had two spells with which London club?

9   England winger who won the League with Chelsea in 2005-06 and had spells with Manchester City before and after that.

10 Northern Ireland goalkeeper who has appeared for Leeds United, Burnley and Sheffield Wednesday.

GLOVE STORY

Questions relating to goalkeepers

1 Who appeared for Tottenham Hotspur and Arsenal, and also played for Northern Ireland against Brazil at the World Cup on his 41st birthday?

2 Jens Martin Knudsen, the bobble hat-wearing goalkeeper, helped which nation achieve draws against Northern Ireland (in 1991) and Scotland (2002)?

3 In 1956 who became the first goalkeeper to be named FWA Footballer of the Year having completed an FA Cup final appearance with a broken neck in that same season?

4 Which two goalkeepers, who played for England at multiple World Cups, had their first two top-flight spells with Leicester City and then Stoke City?

5 Who kept goal in all six matches of England women's triumphant Euro 2022 campaign, conceding only two goals?

6 Middlesbrough (2006) and Fulham (2010) have each played in one European final – and they fielded the same Australian goalkeeper in those matches. Name him.

7 Which former Welsh goalkeeper managed Norwich City to third place in the Premier League in the 1992-93 season?

8 Which goalkeeper represented Great Britain at the 1948 Olympic Games and won the European Cup with Celtic in 1967, and also helped Newcastle United lift the FA Cup twice in the 1950s?

9 Which goalkeeper was a Premier League ever-present in eight consecutive seasons from 2004 to 2012, playing 304 games in that run – the first four with Blackburn Rovers, the next three with Aston Villa and the last with Tottenham Hotspur?

10 Which goalkeeper was on the losing side in FA Cup finals against Arsenal 17 years apart – for Newcastle United in 1998 and for Aston Villa in 2015?

ROUND 63
2003, SKOPJE, MACEDONIA

Wayne Rooney becomes England's youngest goalscorer

Photo courtesy of The Times newspaper

1   How old, in years, was Rooney when his strike against Macedonia in September 2003 made him the youngest England goalscorer?

2   Who was the previous holder of this record?

3   For which club was Rooney a player when he scored this goal?

4   In 2015, against which country did Rooney score his 50th England goal, breaking Sir Bobby Charlton's record?

5   Rooney came out of international retirement to play a friendly against which nation in 2018 – a country where he was playing club football?

6   That match in the picture was a Euro 2004 qualifier that England won 2-1; against which two countries did Rooney score twice at the tournament itself the following summer?

7   By what score did England beat the Macedonians (now known as North Macedonia) in 2023?

FIFTEEN MINUTES OF FAME

Match the FA Cup giant-killers to their victims and the year in question

1   Shrewsbury Town *(tier 4)*, 2003

2   Sutton United *(non-League)*, 1989

3   Colchester United *(tier 4)*, 1971

4   Yeovil Town *(non-League)*, 1949

5   Halifax Town *(tier 4)*, 1980

6   Bradford City *(tier 3)*, 2015

7   Altrincham *(non-League)*, 1986

8   Blyth Spartans *(non-League)*, 1978

9   Harlow Town *(non-League)*, 1980

10 Worcester City *(non-League)*, 1959

11 Bournemouth *(tier 3)*, 1984

12 Lincoln City *(non-League)*, 2017

13 Wrexham *(tier 4)*, 1992

14 Hereford United *(non-League)*, 1972

15 Colchester United *(non-League)*, 1948

A   Leicester City *(tier 2)*

B   Huddersfield Town *(tier 1)*

C   Sunderland *(tier 1)*

D   Arsenal *(tier 1)*

E   Chelsea *(tier 1)*

F   Manchester City *(tier 1)*

G   Leeds United *(tier 1)*

H   Stoke City *(tier 2)*

I   Newcastle United *(tier 1)*

J   Liverpool *(tier 2)*

K   Birmingham City *(tier 1)*

L   Manchester United *(tier 1)*

M   Everton *(tier 1)*

N   Burnley *(tier 1)*

O   Coventry City *(tier 1)*

MATCH OF THE DAY

Identify the players who share the same first and last names

1 (a) Everton right back who played for England at the 1986 World Cup.
(b) Tottenham Hotspur defender or midfielder who played for England at that same World Cup.

2 (a) Yorkshire-born goalkeeper who played 41 times for England and appeared for Leeds United and Tottenham.
(b) Watford and West Bromwich Albion left back who appeared for Birmingham City at the age of 39.

3 (a) England centre back who was captain when Norwich City won the League Cup in 1985 and when Everton lifted the FA Cup in 1995.
(b) England centre back who won the FA Cup with Sunderland in 1973 and the League Cup with Manchester City in 1976.

4 (a) Manchester United midfielder who captained England 65 times.
(b) West Ham United striker who was the top flight's leading scorer in 1972-73.

5 (a) Wolverhampton Wanderers and England defender who became the first player to win 100 caps for any nation.
(b) Centre back who made 198 appearances for Everton between 1978 and 1982.

6 (a) Kept goal for Oxford United when they won the League Cup in 1986.
(b) Brentford midfielder who won nine caps for the Republic of Ireland.

7 (a) Midfielder who won 58 caps for Wales and scored for Fulham in a Europa League semi-final in 2010.
(b) Winger who played 20 times for Manchester United in the 1990s and managed Chester City.

8 (a) Striker who played in the top flight in the 1980s for Sunderland, Watford and West Bromwich Albion, and also appeared for Rangers.
(b) Forward who played a handful of games for Chelsea in the late 1980s.

9 (a) Centre back who played for Derby County, Coventry City and Southampton in the top flight in the 1990s and 2000s.
(b) Full back who played briefly for Coventry in the 1990s.

10 (a) England forward who won 76 caps and spent his entire League career with Preston North End.
(b) Midfielder who played 371 games for Cambridge United.

NICKNAMES

Identify these five fixtures taking place in the 2023-24 Premier League season

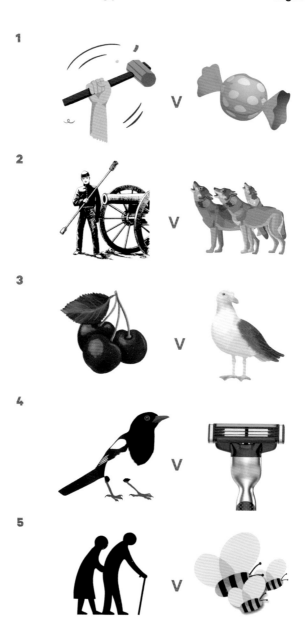

ROUND 67

FIRST THINGS FIRST

Match the year (and month in some cases) with the first time the following occurred

1	Football League games	**A**	1960
2	Fifa World Cup	**B**	1927
3	Three points for a League win	**C**	1991
4	League match with radio commentary (Arsenal v Sheffield United)	**D**	1974
		E	August 1981
5	Women's FA Cup final	**F**	1888
6	League match played on a Sunday	**G**	2019
7	VAR in League	**H**	1958
8	Goal difference (rather than goal average) separated teams level on points in League	**I**	1976
9	Fifa Women's World Cup	**J**	1983
10	League game played on an artificial pitch	**K**	September 1981
11	League match televised live (Blackpool v Bolton Wanderers)	**L**	1968
		M	1930
12	FA Cup final televised in colour in UK	**N**	1920
13	Three League divisions	**O**	1971
14	League was sponsored		
15	Four League tiers		

AROUND THE GROUNDS

Identify these football venues

1   Which ground shares its name with a battle that took place in the north of England in 1066?

2   Which club has a stadium whose name matches that of the "home of golf" (aside from an apostrophe)?

3   Arsenal previously played home matches at Highbury – which League club has a ground with that same name?

4   Which stadium shares its name with a cricket ground half a mile away on the other side of Chester Road?

5   Which club has a stadium that features the name of the city known as the Big Apple?

6   Which team have played home games since 1900 at a ground whose name is a species of shrub or tree?

7   Which two League clubs have the word Valley in their stadium name?

8   Which League ground in Lancashire, whose occupants were relegated from League One in 2023, sounds as if a coronation could take place there?

9   Which League ground in Wales reflects its past use as a horse racing venue?

10   Which two League grounds have "Meadow" in their name?

COMEBACK KINGS

Questions relating to remarkable recoveries

1   Which club did Liverpool beat 4-3 on aggregate in the Champions League semi-finals in 2019 having lost the first leg 3-0 in Spain?

2   Which London club held 3-0 half-time leads at home to Manchester United in 2001 and Manchester City in 2004 yet lost both games – 5-3 to United in the League and 4-3 to a City team who had only ten players throughout the second half?

3   Which team recovered from 5-1 behind – and a man down because of injury – to beat Huddersfield Town 7-6 in 1957 (the only time a side has lost a League game despite scoring six goals)?

4   Which North-East club won 4-3 on aggregate in both the quarter-finals and semi-finals of the Uefa Cup in 2005-06 despite trailing 3-0 each time?

5   Which Manchester United player was among Uruguay's scorers as they hit back from 3-0 down against Senegal to draw 3-3 in a group match at the 2002 World Cup?

6   In 1997 which team recovered from 3-0 down at home to Derby County in the Premier League to triumph 4-3 with a late winner by Lee Bowyer?

7   Which second-tier team overcame a 4-0 first-leg defeat to top-flight Southampton in the League Cup in 1980 by winning the return match 7-1?

8   Tony Hateley scored four goals for which Midlands club as they came back from 5-1 down away to Tottenham Hotspur to draw 5-5 in a League game in 1966?

9   Which London club beat Partizan Belgrade 6-2 in the home leg of a Uefa Cup tie in 1984 yet were eliminated on away goals after losing the second match 4-0?

10   Which team drew 5-5 at home to Everton in 1904 despite having trailed 5-1 at half time?

DRAW YOUR OWN CONCLUSIONS

Identify these post-war England internationals with more than 25 caps

Illustrations courtesy of Susanna Kendal

HANGING UP THEIR BOOTS

Notable careers adopted by footballers after retiring

1   Which Liverpool player, born in South Africa and raised mostly in Australia, designed football boots after his career ended?

2   Mathieu Flamini, the co-founder of a biotechnology company, played for Crystal Palace and which other Premier League club?

3   Which Chelsea and Manchester City player became president of Liberia?

4   What investigative role did Barnsley, Portsmouth and Wigan Athletic defender Arjan de Zeeuw take up when he returned to his native Netherlands?

5   Which emergency service did former Arsenal midfielder David Hillier join?

6   Which Liverpool and Denmark centre back worked as a tattoo artist?

7   Name the Nottingham Forest, Manchester United and England midfielder who subsequently worked as a postman.

8   Ken Monkou became a pancake chef in The Netherlands after playing in the English top flight with Southampton and which other club?

9   Which Southampton, Everton and Wales midfielder became a chemistry and physics teacher?

10   Which Newcastle United and Belgium centre back became a greengrocer?

TRANSFER TURN-UPS

Players who made unexpected moves

1   Danish forward Allan Simonsen, named European Footballer of the Year in 1977, left Barcelona for which second-tier English club at the age of 29?

2   Which striker moved from Queens Park Rangers to Arsenal in the summer of 1980 but quickly left them without making an appearance, joining Crystal Palace?

3   Mo Johnston, the former Watford and Celtic striker, caused a surprise – given that he was a Catholic – by signing for which club in 1989?

4   Which England defender, who had only ever played League football in the Premier League, moved to fourth-tier Notts County in 2009?

5   David Unsworth transferred from West Ham United to Aston Villa in July 1998 but then moved on to which club a month later?

6   Which former Manchester United player ignored their rivalry with Liverpool to join the Anfield club from Inter Milan in 1997?

7   Kevin Keegan, who had won the European Footballer of the Year award in the previous two years while at Hamburg, joined which club in 1980?

8   Which Midlands club signed Croatian Robert Jarni from Real Betis in the summer of 1998 only to sell him on to Real Madrid before he had made an appearance for them?

9   Which former Watford striker joined Manchester United on loan from Shanghai Shenhua in 2020?

10   Which striker, who scored 22 goals for England, left top-flight Chelsea for third tier Notts County at the age of 28 in 1947?

ROUND 73

UNITED FRONT

Identify these current League clubs with United in their name

1   W _ _ _ H _ _   UNITED

2   _ _ _ FF _ _ _ _   UNITED

3   _ _ _ C _ S _ L _   UNITED

4   _ X _ _ _ _   UNITED

5   _ _ N _ H _ S _ _ _   UNITED

6   P _ _ _ _ B _ _ _ _ _ H   UNITED

7   _ EE _ _   UNITED

8   _ _ _ _ _ _ DGE   UNITED

9   _ _ _ _ _ _ HAM   UNITED

10   C _ _ C _ _ _ _ _ _   UNITED

11   _ _ _ L _ _ L _   UNITED

12   _ _ T T _ _   UNITED

FALLEN FROM GRACE

Identify the current ground of these former League clubs. The year in which they left the Football League is given

ROUND 75

RED FACES

Identify these players sent off when playing for England, based on their initials, club and position, the year of their dismissal and their opponents in that match

1   **WR**   -   Manchester United forward   -   2006   -   Portugal

2   **TC**   -   Leeds United defender   -   1977   -   Argentina

3   **AM**   -   Tottenham Hotspur midfielder   -   1968   -   Yugoslavia

4   **RW**   -   AC Milan midfielder   -   1986   -   Morocco

5   **DB**   -   Newcastle United midfielder   -   1999   -   Poland

6   **DB**   -   Manchester United midfielder   -   1998   -   Argentina

7   **SG**   -   Liverpool midfielder   -   2012   -   Ukraine

8   **AB**   -   Arsenal midfielder   -   1973   -   Poland

9   **RG**   -   West Ham United goalkeeper   -   2009   -   Ukraine

10   **AS**   -   Leeds United forward   -   2002   -   FYR Macedonia

11   **RJ**   -   Chelsea defender   -   2020   -   Denmark

12   **PI**   -   Liverpool midfielder   -   1998   -   Sweden

13   **LS**   -   Manchester United defender   -   2023   -   Italy

14   **RS**   -   Liverpool forward   -   2014   -   Ecuador

15   **PS**   -   Manchester United midfielder   -   1999   -   Sweden

WAIT FOR IT!

When matches were delayed

1   Which two EFL Trophy fixtures were played on the weekend of March 13 and 14, 2021?

2   Why did the referee require some paint to be found before the match between Derby County and Manchester City in April 1977 could resume?

3   Which London club's match away to Gillingham in April 2023 was delayed for 20 minutes because of floodlight failure – and as they emerged from the tunnel to complete the match they celebrated a promotion which arose from a result going their way elsewhere?

4   When the appearance of a dog on the pitch held up England's World Cup quarter-final against Brazil in 1962, which England player caught the canine intruder?

5   The first League Cup final between Aston Villa and Rotherham United was held over until the following season because of fixture congestion – in which year did it take place?

6   Which London club had their opening match of the 1988-89 season postponed only hours before kick-off because building work on their stadium had yet to be completed?

7   Which English team arrived late for two Champions League games in a row at their own ground in October 2018 because of heavy traffic – kick-off was delayed for the first of those?

8   England's friendly match against Honduras in Miami was halted for three quarters of an hour during the first half because of a thunderstorm – for which World Cup was the fixture a warm-up?

9   In which season did cold weather force a series of postponements that meant seven FA Cup third-round fixtures were only played more than five weeks after the fourth round had begun?

10   Why was the Manchester United-Bournemouth match that was scheduled for the final day of the 2015-16 season put back two days?

O' MY WORD

Identify these players and managers whose surnames start with O'

1   Manchester United defender who won 118 Ireland caps between 2001 and 2018.

2   Nottingham Forest and Northern Ireland midfielder who managed the Republic of Ireland.

3   Arsenal's record appearance holder who went on to manage Leeds United and Aston Villa.

4   Scottish forward who won the League title with Derby County and Nottingham Forest under Brian Clough and also played for that manager at Leeds United.

5   Manager praised for steering Bournemouth away from relegation danger in 2022-23, their first season back in the Premier League.

6   Republic of Ireland winger who helped Ipswich Town win the Uefa Cup.

7   Irishman who managed Manchester United in the early 1970s.

8   Republic of Ireland centre back who played in the Premier League for Bradford City, Newcastle United, Portsmouth and Bolton Wanderers.

9   Manager who returned for a second spell in charge of Northern Ireland in 2022.

10   Welsh winger who made 491 appearances for Brighton & Hove Albion (with a name almost identical to that of a longstanding BBC television horse racing commentator).

NATIONAL PARKS

Identify the clubs with Park in the name of their ground and locate the grounds on the map

1   Adams Park

2   Brunton Park

3   Dens Park

4   Edgeley Park

5   Ewood Park

6   Fratton Park

7   Goodison Park

8   Home Park

9   Rugby Park

10   Selhurst Park

11   Somerset Park

12   St James Park

13   Villa Park

14   Vale Park

WHAT'S MY LINE?

Players and managers with jobs or professions as their surnames

1   Ipswich Town and Rangers centre back who played for England at World Cups in 1982, 1986 and 1990.

2   Club for whom midfielder Phil Barber played in the 1990 FA Cup final.

3   Manager who left Brighton & Hove Albion for Chelsea in 2022.

4   England forward who played for Arsenal and Torino and also had two spells with Hibernian.

5   Club for whom Richard Carpenter made 279 appearances early this century.

6   Tottenham Hotspur's caretaker manager in the 2021 League Cup final.

7   Scored for England in their 3-1 win over France at the 1982 World Cup, the fifth consecutive game in which he had netted for his country.

8   Craig Gardner and his brother Gary Gardner have both played for which two West Midlands clubs this century?

9   Position in which Siobhan Chamberlain won 50 caps for the England women's team.

10   Liverpool-born manager who has taken charge of Accrington Stanley, Chesterfield, Portsmouth, Wigan Athletic and Ipswich Town.

CLIMATE CONTROL

Players and managers with "weather-related" surnames

1   Chinese defender who played 151 times for Manchester City from 2002 to 2008.

2   Dominic Blizzard helped which club gain promotion to the Premier League in 2006?

3   Fulham and West Ham United centre back who later won the League title in 1995 with Blackburn Rovers at the age of 35.

4   Jonas Wind played for which country against England in the Euro 2020 semi-finals?

5   Pepe Reina played in goal for Liverpool from 2005 to 2013 but returned to the Premier League with which club in 2020?

6   George Snow made more than 200 appearances for which Welsh club in the 1930s?

7   Ray McHale managed which Yorkshire club for six years from 1989?

8   Izale McLeod scored 60 goals for which club in the first three years of their existence?

9   What nationality was Bob Stormont, who played for Preston North End in the 1890s?

10   Billy Fogg helped which Yorkshire club reach the 1930 FA Cup final?

TAYLOR-MADE QUESTIONS

Give the first name of each Taylor

1   Blackburn Rovers, Birmingham City, Bolton Wanderers and Bury winger who was chief executive of the Professional Footballers' Association for 40 years.

2   Scored both goals for West Ham United in their 2-0 win over Fulham in the 1975 FA Cup final.

3   Won all of his four England caps while in the third tier with Crystal Palace in 1976 and, as caretaker manager of his country in 2000, made David Beckham captain of England for the first time.

4   Manchester United and England centre forward who died in the Munich air disaster in 1958.

5   When Exeter City met Walsall in October 2021 what full name – both first name and surname – did the two managers share?

6   Goalkeeper who won 88 Northern Ireland caps and played for Fulham in the third and then second tier and finally the Premier League.

7   Swansea City left back who reached the Euro 2016 semi-finals with Wales.

8   Midfielder who made nearly 300 appearances for Aston Villa between 1994 and 2003.

9   Immediate predecessor to Bill Shankly as Liverpool manager.

10   Which defender captained the Swindon Town team who finished bottom of the Premier League in 1993-94?

2005, ISTANBUL

Steven Gerrard greets the Champions League trophy

Photo courtesy of The Times newspaper

1   Which team did Liverpool beat in the 2005 Champions League final?

2   Liverpool conceded a goal to which legendary defender in the first minute of this match?

3   What number did Gerrard wear in this game?

4   In Liverpool's final Champions League group match earlier in that season, against which team did Gerrard score the decisive late goal that took his side into the knock-out phase?

5   How many League titles did Gerrard win during his 17 seasons as a Liverpool player?

6   A year later Liverpool won another final in the same manner – via a penalty shoot-out after a 3-3 draw in which Gerrard scored. Who were their FA Cup final victims on that occasion?

7   In 2023 Gerrard was appointed as manager of Al-Ettifaq, a club based in which country?

TENANCY AGREEMENT

Clubs who moved into a temporary home

1   On which ground did Manchester United play home matches in the first four seasons after the Second World War because their own Old Trafford stadium had been bombed?

2   Which club played their first four top-flight home games of the 1971-72 season away from their own ground as punishment for hooliganism (they played two at Hillsborough and one each at Boothferry Park, Hull, and Leeds Road, Huddersfield)?

3   Who were Tottenham Hotspur's opponents in their last match at their temporary home of Wembley in March 2019 before they moved into their new stadium – the match drew an attendance of 81,332, the second-highest top-flight attendance ever?

4   During Charlton Athletic's absence from The Valley from 1985 to 1992 they spent six years playing home games at Selhurst Park and one year at which other London ground?

5   Why did Queens Park Rangers play two Uefa Cup home games in 1984 at Highbury rather than at their own Loftus Road ground?

6   Which club used Loftus Road as a home ground between 2002 and 2004 while their own stadium was being developed?

7   When Manchester United were ordered to play a Cup Winners' Cup home game against Saint-Etienne at least 200 miles from Old Trafford, which club's ground did they choose?

8   In the early 1990s which League club played home matches at Macclesfield Town's Moss Rose ground (Macclesfield was then a non-League club)?

9   Which club played successive home fixtures at the stadiums of Preston North End, Blackburn Rovers and Blackpool during the 2015-16 season when their own ground was flooded?

10   Which club played home games at Gillingham's Priestfield Stadium for two seasons in the late 1990s after their own ground had been sold?

SINGING FROM THE SAME SHEET (VERSE 2)

Identify the name shared by the musical artist or band who performed the song and the player/manager/club described

1. (a) Song: What a Wonderful World.
   (b) Tottenham Hotspur and Watford striker who scored Northern Ireland's goal in the World Cup win over hosts Spain in 1982.

2. (a) Song: The Best.
   (b) Goalkeeper who played for Manchester United and then helped Sheffield Wednesday beat United in the 1991 League Cup final by keeping a clean sheet.

3. (a) Song: How Am I Supposed to Live Without You.
   (b) Club for whom Nat Lofthouse scored 287 goals and was later managed by him.

4. (a) Song: White Christmas.
   (b) North-easterner who managed Sunderland in their defeat to Liverpool in the 1992 FA Cup final.

5. (a) Song: Because of You.
   (b) Substitute who scored England's winning goal in the Women's Euro 2022 final.

6. (a) Song: Mona Lisa.
   (b) Premier League's top scorer in 1993-94 who left Newcastle United for Manchester United in 1995.

7. (a) Song: In the Air Tonight.
   (b) Everton and Fulham midfielder who scored a penalty for Scotland against Brazil in the opening match of the 1998 World Cup.

8. (a) Song: Don't It Make My Brown Eyes Blue.
   (b) Club on whose ground Wimbledon and Charlton Athletic played as tenants in the 1990s.

9. (a) Song: King of the Road.
   (b) Cameroon forward who played at the 1994 World Cup age 42 and who had faced England in the quarter-finals at the tournament four years earlier.

10. (a) Song: Stand by Me.
    (b) Centre back or midfielder who spent his whole career at Tottenham Hotspur and played for England at the 2010 World Cup.

CROSSING BORDERS

Name the countries to which these players switched allegiance after first playing for the nation mentioned

1   Steve Caulker, England

2   Nacer Chadli, Morocco

3   Wilfried Zaha, England

4   Diego Costa, Brazil

5   Declan Rice, Republic of Ireland

6   Denzel Dumfries, Aruba

7   Kristy Moore, Australia (women)

8   Mario Fernandes, Brazil

9   Jermaine Jones, Germany

10   Jackie Sewell, England

11   Alex Bruce, Republic of Ireland

12   Gordon Hodgson, South Africa

13   Helder Costa, Portugal

14   Ken Armstrong, England

15   Vurnon Anita, Netherlands

COMBAT QUESTIONS

Football's links with the two World Wars

1 Which club was reigning champions during both the First and Second World Wars, having won the League titles of 1914-15 and 1938-39?

2 As compensation for the absence of a Football League season in 1945-46 immediately after the Second World War, what temporary change of format was made to the FA Cup in that campaign?

3 Which south coast club's 10-0 home win over Northampton Town in September 1939 would have remained their biggest victory had the results in that aborted season not been wiped from the records after the outbreak of war?

4 What war-related purpose did Swindon Town's County Ground serve during the Second World War?

5 What name is sometimes given to the 1915 FA Cup final to reflect the large number of uniformed soldiers watching the match?

6 England played 36 unofficial matches during and just after the Second World War, from 1939 to 1946. Which player made the most appearances – 29 – in those games?

7 Denis Compton fought in India during the Second World War and won the League title with which club both before and after that war?

8 Which player scored 29 goals for England but retired from senior football after sustaining injuries when fighting in the First World War?

9 During the Second World War which London ground was a first-aid training centre and a headquarters for Air Raid Precautions?

10 Which England player won the Military Medal for his contribution to the First World War and later edited the football magazine that took his own name?

THE KEEPER HAS SCORED!

Goalkeepers who were also goalscorers

1   Whose goal at a corner against Plymouth Argyle in the third minute of stoppage time saved Carlisle United from being relegated out of the League on the last day of the 1998-99 season?

2   Which Northern Irish goalkeeper scored for Tottenham Hotspur from a clearance in the 1967 Charity Shield match against Manchester United?

3   The only two goals by goalkeepers in the top division in the 1980s were scored by Steve Ogrizovic and Steve Sherwood. For which Midlands club did Ogrizovic score against Sheffield Wednesday in 1986 – the same club against whom Sherwood scored for Watford in 1984?

4   Which goalkeeper was on the mark for Manchester United against Rotor Volgograd in 1995 and for Aston Villa against Everton in 2001?

5   Which future Liverpool goalkeeper scored a penalty for Crewe Alexandra in 1980?

6   Which Stoke City goalkeeper scored from a wind-assisted clearance after 13 seconds of a Premier League match against Southampton in 2013?

7   Alisson headed a late winning goal for Liverpool away to which club in 2021?

8   Which American goalkeeper scored a late equaliser at a corner for Blackburn Rovers in 2004, only to then concede a winner for Charlton Athletic moments later?

9   Which goalkeeper scored two penalties for Manchester United in the top division in 1973?

10   Which goalkeeper scored for Hull City in two different League games in the 1994-95 season when being fielded as an emergency striker?

ROUND 88

WEMBLEY WIZARDS

Questions on the national stadium

1 Which pair of clubs contested two of the first three FA Cup semi-finals to be held at Wembley, in 1991 and 1993?

2 Who scored the winning goal in both the 1923 and 1926 FA Cup finals for Bolton Wanderers, the former being the first ever goal scored at Wembley?

3 More than 80,000 watched which two fourth-tier teams contest the final of the Football League Trophy (then known as the Associate Members' Cup) in 1988?

4 Which club won the 1964 FA Cup final at Wembley and a year later lifted the Cup Winners' Cup at the same ground?

5 Which London club, then in the Third Division South, played two home matches at Wembley in the 1930-31 season while work took place on their own ground?

6 Which player, as of June 2023, had scored a record 52 goals at Wembley for League clubs or the England men's team – more than twice as many as any other player? He was helped by the fact that his club played home matches there for a couple of years.

7 A crowd of 87,192 watched England beat which nation at Wembley in the final of the Women's Euro 2022?

8 Which team did England beat 8-0 at Wembley in 1987, three years after winning away to the same opponents by the same scoreline?

9 Which top-flight club played three times at Wembley in the space of four weeks in March-April 1988: in the finals of the League Cup and Full Members' Cup and in the Football League Centenary Tournament?

10 Who scored the winning goal for Arsenal in the FA Cup finals of 2014 (against Hull City) and 2017 (against Chelsea), with both of those goals coming 11 minutes from the end of the match (ignoring stoppage time)?

COMING HOME

Footballers born overseas but who played for England

1   Name the Jamaica-born forward who grew up close to Wembley Stadium.

2   Which midfielder, born in Canada, won 39 England caps before his first appearance in the English League in 2007?

3   Terry Butcher, who played 77 times for England, was born in which south-east Asian country?

4   Which centre forward, born in French Guiana, scored the BBC's Goal of the Season in 1981-82 for West Bromwich Albion against Norwich City?

5   Which Watford striker, born in Jamaica, scored a hat-trick against Luxembourg on his first start for England in 1982?

6   John Salako, who played for Crystal Palace in the defeat to Manchester United in the 1990 FA Cup final, was born in which African nation?

7   Which defender, who has played for Chelsea and AC Milan, was born in the city that staged the 1988 Winter Olympic Games?

8   Colin Viljoen, born in South Africa, made 372 appearances for which club between 1967 and 1978?

9   Which Jamaica-born player scored a famous goal for England away to Brazil in 1984 after a long, mazy run?

10   Name the Johannesburg-born winger who scored the stoppage-time winning goal in the 1953 FA Cup final – dubbed the "Matthews Cup final" – in which his Blackpool team beat Bolton Wanderers 4-3.

ROUND 90

RECENT EVENTS

Questions relating to the 2022-23 season

1 Which club led the Premier League table for a total of 248 days, the most in top-flight history by any team who were not champions in that season?

2 Who scored for Manchester City after 12 seconds of the FA Cup final against Manchester United, the fastest ever goal in the fixture?

3 Which Premier League club won more matches in European competition than in the League, FA Cup and League Cup combined (14 to 13)?

4 Whose appointment by Crystal Palace made him the oldest ever top-flight manager at the age of 75?

5 Which club was promoted to the Premier League to become the first to travel from top flight to non-League and back again since the introduction of four tiers in 1958?

6 Which player contributed four of the eight hat-tricks scored in the Premier League during this season?

7 Which team had two players and their manager sent off in an FA Cup defeat away to Manchester United?

8 Which four Premier League players started the World Cup final for Argentina?

9 Which club gave 48.1 per cent of their League starts to Portuguese players to become the team most dominated by one non-British Isles nationality over one top-flight season in history?

10 Which Yorkshire club stayed put in the Championship, finishing 19th, having moved between the second and third tiers in each of the previous six seasons?

THE AWARDS CEREMONY

Questions relating to annual player awards

1 In 1979-80 which Liverpool player became the first to win the double of FWA Footballer of the Year and PFA Players' Player of the Year in the same season?

2 Which striker was FWA Footballer of the Year with Everton in 1985-86 and with Tottenham Hotspur in 1991-92?

3 Leeds United centre-back Norman Hunter was the first winner of the PFA Players' Player of the Year award, receiving his award in Don Revie's last season as manager of the club. What was that season?

4 Which English club supplied different winners of the Ballon D'Or (also known as the European Footballer of the Year award) in 1964, 1966 and 1968?

5 Which West Ham midfielder was named FWA Footballer of the Year in 2010-11, a season in which his club finished bottom of the Premier League?

6 Which club supplied different winners of the FWA Footballer of the Year and PFA Player of the Year awards in 1980-81?

7 Fran Kirby won the PFA Women's Players' Player of the Year award in 2017-18 and 2020-21 – for which club was she playing?

8 Syd Owen was FWA Footballer of the Year in 1958-59 as a player at a club who were far from traditional heavyweights. Name that club.

9 Who is the only English player to have won the Ballon D'Or since 1980?

10 Who was PFA Players' Player of the Year with different clubs in 1994-95 and 1996-97?

ROUND 92
CLUB LEGENDS
Identify the players from their statues

Photos courtesy of footballstadiumphotography.co.uk

BIG MACS

Players and managers with Mac/Mc surnames

1   Northern Irish midfielder who played for Manchester United from 1971 to 1982.

2   Scored all of England's goals in their 5-0 win at home to Cyprus in 1975.

3   Manager of Southampton when they won the FA Cup in 1976 as a second-tier team.

4   Ireland player at the 1990 and 1994 World Cup who appeared for Manchester United and Aston Villa.

5   Club that Dave Mackay managed to the League title in 1975.

6   Appointed as Manchester United manager in 1969 when Sir Matt Busby retired.

7   When Brian McDermott managed Leeds United from April 2013 to May 2014 another Brian McDermott was in charge of a different major sports team in that city. Which sport?

8   Club for whom Stuart McCall scored two equalising goals in their 3-2 defeat to Liverpool in the 1989 FA Cup final.

9   Position in which Abbie McManus played for England at the 2019 Women's World Cup, where her team reached the semi-finals.

10   Club whose ground features the Jimmy McIlroy Stand, named after a player who helped them win the League title in 1960.

CROSSING THE DIVIDE

Managers who guided two fierce local rivals

1 Who has managed all three of the following pairs of rivals: Newcastle United and Sunderland; Aston Villa and Birmingham City; and Sheffield United and Sheffield Wednesday?

2 Ernest Mangnall managed in 22 derbies between these two city rivals, 11 for each team. Name those clubs.

3 George Graham and Terry Neill have both managed Arsenal and Tottenham Hotspur. Which of these North London clubs did Graham lead first and which did Neill guide first?

4 Who appeared for West Ham United for 21 years – playing in the top division at the age of 41 – before managing them and their big rivals Millwall?

5 William Barclay managed a club in the inaugural League season of 1888-89 and was also in charge of their close neighbours in their first three League campaigns, from 1893. Which were the clubs?

6 Which World Cup winner with England in 1966 later managed south-coast rivals Portsmouth and Southampton?

7 Which Scot has managed East Anglian rivals Norwich City and Ipswich Town since the turn of the century?

8 John Ward and Terry Cooper both managed the main two clubs in which city?

9 Lancashire neighbours Burnley and Blackburn Rovers have been managed by which Scotland-born Republic of Ireland striker?

10 Brian Little and Ronnie Allen both took charge of which two West Midlands rivals?

HONOURS BOARD

Identify the season from these trophy winners

1   *League champions:* Manchester City. *FA Cup winners:* Manchester City. *League Cup winners:* Manchester City.

2   *League champions:* Liverpool. *FA Cup winners:* Wimbledon. *League Cup winners:* Luton Town.

3   *League champions:* Manchester United. *FA Cup winners:* Wigan Athletic. *League Cup winners:* Swansea City.

4   *League champions:* Derby County. *FA Cup winners:* Leeds United. *League Cup winners:* Stoke City.

5   *League champions:* Manchester United. *FA Cup winners:* Manchester City. *League Cup winners:* Birmingham City.

6   *League champions:* Leeds United. *FA Cup winners:* Manchester City. *League Cup winners:* Swindon Town.

7   *League champions:* Nottingham Forest. *FA Cup winners:* Ipswich Town. *League Cup winners:* Nottingham Forest.

8   *League champions:* Manchester United. *FA Cup winners:* Portsmouth. *League Cup winners:* Tottenham Hotspur.

9   *League champions:* Everton. *FA Cup winners:* Manchester United. *League Cup winners:* Norwich City.

10 *League champions:* Liverpool. *FA Cup winners:* Sunderland. *League Cup winners:* Tottenham Hotspur.

11 *League champions:* Liverpool. *FA Cup winners:* Everton. *League Cup winners:* West Bromwich Albion.

12 *League champions:* Leeds United. *FA Cup winners:* Liverpool. *League Cup winners:* Wolverhampton Wanderers.

13 *League champions:* Manchester United. *FA Cup winners:* Tottenham Hotspur. *League Cup winners:* Queens Park Rangers.

14 *League champions:* Liverpool. *FA Cup winners:* Liverpool. *League Cup winners:* Oxford United.

15 *League champions:* Tottenham Hotspur. *FA Cup winners:* Tottenham Hotspur. *League Cup winners:* Aston Villa.

2016, KING POWER STADIUM, LEICESTER

Jamie Vardy's Premier League triumph

Photo courtesy of The Times newspaper

1 How old was Jamie Vardy when Leicester City clinched the League title in only his second season as a top-flight player?

2 In how many consecutive League games did Vardy score early in that 2015-16 campaign, one short of the top-flight record?

3 In which Yorkshire city was Vardy born?

4 Which team did Leicester beat 3-1 at home on the day they were presented with the Premier League trophy?

5 From which then-non-League club did Vardy join Leicester City in 2012?

6 Against which club did Vardy score a Premier League hat-trick in both December 2016 and September 2020?

7 Which nation did Vardy score against at Euro 2016?

STAND FOR THE ANTHEMS, PLEASE

Identify the club from their associated song

1   You'll Never Walk Alone

2   Glad All Over

3   Blue is the Colour

4   Going Home (Theme of the Local Hero)

5   Marching on Together

6   On the Ball City

7   Blue Moon

8   When the Saints Go Marching In

9   Z Cars theme

10   I'm Forever Blowing Bubbles

11   The Greasy Chip Butty Song

12   Sky Blue Song

13   Delilah

14   No One Likes Us

15   The Red, Red Robin

FANCY SEEING YOU HERE

Identify the clubs who found themselves in unexpected surroundings

1   Which Wiltshire club conceded 100 goals in their only top-flight season of 1993-94?

2   Whose only European campaign came as a second-tier club in 2004-05 – they qualified for the Uefa Cup as FA Cup runners-up?

3   Which team's fans sang "It's just like watching Brazil" during their club's only top-division season, in 1997-98?

4   Which Midlands club were champions in 1958 and 1959 yet had sunk to the fourth tier by 1986?

5   Which club, based in east London, had their sole top-flight campaign in 1962-63?

6   The 1991-92 champions spent three consecutive seasons in the third tier from 2007 as they suffered from financial problems. Name them.

7   Which club lost 6-1 away to Bayern Munich in October 1970 in their only season in European competition?

8   Which club did manager David Bowen guide from fourth tier to top flight, overseeing what remains their only season in the top division in 1965-66?

9   Which was the only Premier League team to reach the quarter-finals of the 2016-17 Champions League?

10   Which club, who have since won multiple Premier League titles, only escaped from the third tier by beating Gillingham in a play-off final in 1999?

JUST JOHNSONS

Give the first name of each Johnson

1   Ipswich Town striker who later won four League titles with Liverpool.

2   Forward who scored 11 Premier League penalties for Crystal Palace during their relegation season of 2004-05.

3   England right back who won trophies with Chelsea, Portsmouth and Liverpool.

4   Derby County and Leeds United midfielder who played once for England.

5   Managed Bristol City – as did his son – and also took charge of the Latvia national team.

6   Striker who played for Derby County, Aston Villa and Celtic in the 1990s.

7   The record goalscorer for both Sheffield United and Mansfield Town.

8   Birmingham City midfielder who won 56 caps for Northern Ireland.

9   West Ham United full back who came through the club's youth system.

10 Centre back who lost the 2008 FA Cup final with Cardiff but won the 2011 League Cup final with Birmingham City, and later joined Wolverhampton Wanderers.

LAST HURRAH

Notable final games

1 In Southampton's final match at the Dell in 2001 which player scored their 89th-minute winner in a 3-2 win over Arsenal?

2 Which club drew 5-5 away to West Bromwich Albion in 2013 in their final match under their long-serving Scottish manager?

3 Which player scored a hat-trick for Arsenal against Wigan Athletic in 2006 in their final fixture at Highbury?

4 Who resigned as England manager after suffering defeat in his country's last match played at the old Wembley Stadium in October 2000?

5 Whose last match before resigning as Liverpool manager in February 1991 was a 4-4 draw away to Everton in an FA Cup replay?

6 Who clinched promotion to the Premier League in 1995 by winning their final match at their Ayrsome Park ground?

7 Whose final appearance for Arsenal in August 2017 came in a 4-0 defeat away to the Liverpool team he was about to join?

8 In Wimbledon's last match at Plough Lane in May 1991 they lost 3-0 to the club who were about to become their landlords. Name that latter club.

9 In which player's final appearance for Manchester United did he captain them to the Champions League triumph that completed the treble?

10 Which club beat Derby County 6-2 in 2005 in their final match at Highfield Road, their home for more than a century?

ANSWERS

All answers have been researched as correct at September 8th 2023.

1. FIRST IMPRESSIONS

1. Arsenal, 2. Bill Nicholson, 3. Sir Bobby Robson, 4. It was the first League match played in an all-seater stadium, 5. Fabrizio Ravanelli, 6. Everton, 7. Barnet, 8. Jonathan Woodgate, 9. France, 10. Tony Cottee

2. THE NAME'S THE SAME

1. Mick Mills and Danny Mills, 2. Joe Allen and Clive Allen, 3. Ben White and Ellen White, 4. Kevin Phillips and David Phillips, 5. Peter Barnes and John Barnes, 6. John Charles and Gary Charles, 7. Emlyn Hughes and Mark Hughes, 8. Eddie Newton and Keith Newton, 9. Andy Gray and Eddie Gray, 10. Nick Henry and Thierry Henry

3. STARTING POINTS

1. (J), 2. (M), 3. (E), 4. (N), 5. (O), 6. (H), 7. (K), 8. (A), 9. (F), 10. (B), 11. (I), 12. (C), 13. (L), 14. (G), 15. (D)

4. HAPPY FAMILIES (PART 1)

1. 2, 2. Justin Fashanu (Norwich) and John Fashanu (Wimbledon), 3. Norwich City (Bryan Gunn) and Manchester United (Peter Schmeichel), 4. Derby County, 5: Reece James and Lauren James, 6. Cardiff City, 7. Brian Little (Stoke) and Alan Little (York), 8. Kevin Bond, son of John Bond, 9, Peter Knowles, 10. Roy Bailey. His son is Gary Bailey

5. RESTRICTED VIEWS

1. Crystal Palace, 2. Tottenham Hotspur, 3. Manchester United, 4. Watford, 5. Sheffield United, 6. Nottingham Forest, 7. Leicester City, 8. Fulham, 9. Manchester City, 10. Everton

6. HOLY ORDERS

1. Saracens, 2. Nick Pope, 3. Wales, 4. Graham Cross, 5. Derek Temple, 6. Dixie Dean, 7. Bishop Auckland, 8. West Ham United 9. Barnsley, 10. Leicester City

7. CELEBRITY FANS

1. (K), 2. (N), 3. (G), 4. (I), 5. (C), 6. (B), 7. (E), 8. (M), 9. (H), 10. (J), 11. (L), 12. (F), 13. (O), 14. (D), 15. (A)

8. MEDIA MATTERS

1. Kenneth Wolstenholme, 2. Michael Thomas, 3. Sir Bobby Robson, 4. Teddy Sheringham, 5. Wimbledon, the winners, and Liverpool, 6. Swedes 2, Turnips 1, 7. David Coleman, 8. David Beckham, 9. Peter Jones, 10. Francis Lee

9. DICTIONARY DEFINITIONS

1. Gary Speed, 2. Peter Crouch, 3. Nicky Butt, 4. Robbie Savage, 5. David Seaman, 6. John Scales, 7. Dennis Wise, 8. David Batty, 9. Roger Hunt, 10. Jimmy Hill, 11. Dan Burn, 12. Ben Foster

10. DOUBLE FIGURES

1. Manchester United, 2. Manchester City, 3. Gillingham, 4. West Ham United, 5. Bournemouth, 6. Leeds United, 7. Newport County, 8. Notts County, 9. Fulham, 10. Aston Villa

11. MAPPING IT OUT

1. Alan Sunderland (D), 2. Dion Dublin (G), 3. Gareth Southgate (K), 4. Clarke Carlisle (E), 5. Bob Paisley (B), 6. James Chester (H), 7. Chris Sutton (N), 8. Shaun Derry (C), 9. Kevin Poole (O), 10. Justin Edinburgh (A), 11. Solly March (I), 12. Neville Southall (L), 13. Alan Cork (J), 14. Bryan Douglas (F), 15. Alan Slough (M)

12. BLUE BLOODS

1. Leicester City, 2. Reading, 3. Pepe Reina, 4. Doncaster Rovers, 5. Bob Lord, 6. Bradford City, 7. Mark Noble, 8. Liverpool, 9. Alan Knight, 10. Crystal Palace

13. MEET THE SMITHS

1. Alan Smith, 2. Mike Smith, 3. Delia Smith, 4. Bobby Smith, 5. Sue Smith, 6. Jim Smith, 7. Alan Smith, 8. Tommy Smith, 9. Kelly Smith, 10. Dean Smith

14. IT TAKES ALL SPORTS

1. Boxing, 2. Clive Allen, 3. Mick Channon, 4. Stanley Matthews, 5. Petr Cech, 6. Craven Cottage, 7. Baseball Ground, 8. Rock of Gibraltar, 9. Gareth Bale, 10. CB Fry

15. GENERAL KNOWLEDGE

1. John Terry, 2. Lee Dixon, 3. Stewart Downing, 4. Rio Ferdinand, 5. Tim Sherwood, 6. Gareth Barry, 7. Sol Campbell, 8. John Barnes, 9. Bobby Moore, 10. Nigel Worthington

16. 1966, WEMBLEY

1. Second (Martin Peters scored it), 2. Swiss, 3. Argentina, 4. Kylian Mbappé, 5. Stoke City, 6. Chelsea, 7. Sir Bobby Charlton

17. PRIME MINISTER'S QUESTION TIME

1. Ian Callaghan (Jim Callaghan), 2. Ray Wilson (Harold Wilson), 3. Ben Thatcher (Margaret Thatcher), 4. Tony Brown (Gordon Brown), 5. Mark Chamberlain (Neville Chamberlain), 6. Andy Blair (Tony Blair), 7. David May (Theresa May), 8. Adrian Heath (Edward Heath), 9. Brennan Johnson (Boris Johnson), 10. Denis Law (Bonar Law)

18. TREATMENT ROOM

1. A sign warning players not to warm up in the goalmouth, 2. Steve Morrow, 3. A dog ran into him as he gathered the ball, 4. David Batty, 5. Dave Beasant, 6. By shouting at the defenders on his team, 7. Southampton, 8. He got his foot caught in the net when retrieving some balls, 9. A puddle of wee left by his dog, 10. David James

19. TEST YOUR GEOGRAPHY

1. Newcastle United, 2. Chelsea, 3. Southampton, 4. Wrexham, 5. Gillingham, 6. Shrewsbury Town, 7. Stoke City, 8. Bristol City, 9. Barrow, 10. Plymouth Argyle, 11. Brighton & Hove Albion, 12. Carlisle United

20. WHAT'S THE "SCORE"?

1. Manchester United, 2. 1995, 3. United's Diogo Dalot and Liverpool's Diogo Jota, 4. Manchester City, 5. Latvia, 6. West Bromwich Albion, 7. Leon Clarke, 8. Chelsea, 9. Jack Charlton, 10. FC Twente

21. SEEING DOUBLE

1. Ian Wright and Mark Bright, 2. Aston Villa, 3. Darren and Marcus, 4. Newcastle United, 5. Chris Waddle, 6. Wigan Athletic, 7. Reading, 8. Joe Cole and Carlton Cole, 9: Mark Stein, 10: Forest Green Rovers

22. FOUNDER MEMBERS

1. Burnley, 2. Everton, 3. West Bromwich Albion, 4. Blackburn Rovers, 5. Wolves, 6. Bolton Wanderers, 7. Preston North End, 8. Stoke City, 9. Notts County, 10. Aston Villa, 11. Derby County

23. BIG FISH IN A SMALL POND

1. Armenia, 2. Emmanuel Adebayor, 3. Goalkeeper, 4. Dwight Yorke, 5. Kenya, 6. Alexander Hleb, 7. Liberia, 8. Pierre-Emerick Aubameyang, 9. Tanzania, 10. Philippines

24. THE BIG SCREEN

1. Bend it like Beckham, 2. Arsenal, 3. Looking for Eric, 4. Ipswich Town, 5. Gregory's Girl, 6. The 1966 World Cup final, 7. Vinnie Jones, 8. The Damned United, 9. The United States, 10. The Arsenal Stadium Mystery

25. MATCH ABANDONED

1. Denis Law, 2. Fog, 3. Derby County, 4. Manchester United, 5. Sheffield United had been reduced to six men by three red cards and two injuries – games must be abandoned if one team has only six players, 6. Terry Venables, 7. Heavy snow, 8. Wimbledon, 9. Argentina, 10. Vicarage Road – Watford v Wigan Athletic

26. SINGING FROM THE SAME SHEET (VERSE 1)

1. Rolling Stones; John Stones, 2. John Lennon; Neil Lennon, 3. Fleetwood Mac; Fleetwood Town, 4. Taylor Swift; Peter Taylor, 5. Right Said Fred; Fred, 6. Whitney Houston; Stewart Houston, 7. Alice Cooper; Terry Cooper, 8. Pharrell Williams; Fara Williams, 9. Walker Brothers; Des Walker, 10. Danny Wilson; Danny Wilson

27. EMOJI TIME

1. David Silva, 2. Illkay Gundogan, 3. Allison, 4. Angel Di Maria, 5. Fred, 6. John Hartson, 7. Tony Adams, 8. Aaron Ramsey, 9. Harry Kane, 10. Mario Ballotelli

11. Luton Town, 12. Crystal Palace, 13. Queens Park Rangers, 14. Wolverhampton Wanderers, 15. Blackburn Rovers, 16. Southampton, 17. Bolton Wanderers, 18. Reading, 19. Wrexham, 20. West Ham United

28. KEEPING UP WITH THE JONESES

1. Nathan Jones, 2. Joey Jones, 3. Phil Jones, 4. Mick Jones, 5. Cliff Jones, 6. Dave Jones, 7. Brad Jones, 8. Cobi Jones, 9. Curtis Jones, 10. Graeme Jones

29. CHRISTMAS GREETINGS

1. Blackpool and Blackburn Rovers – Blackpool won 4-2, 2. Sheffield Wednesday, 3. Queens Park Rangers, 4. Sheffield United 5. Roque Santa Cruz, 6. Gary McAllister, 7. The 1970s – two games were played in 1976, 8. Alan Pardew, 9. Fulham, 10. Leeds United

30. GONE CLUBBING

1. Leicester City, 2. Stoke City, 3. West Ham United, 4. Plymouth Argyle, 5. Birmingham City, 6. Chesterfield, 7. Watford, 8. Leyton Orient, 9. Ipswich Town, 10. Coventry City

31. 1998, SAINT-ETIENNE

1. Diego Simeone, 2. Michael Owen, 3. Paul Ince and David Batty, 4. Wayne Rooney, 5. Los Angeles Galaxy, 6. Arsenal, 7. Austria

32. EURO HEROES

1. (J), 2. (O), 3. (F), 4. (A), 5. (L), 6. (B), 7. (C), 8. (D), 9. (E), 10. (I), 11. (M), 12. (N), 13. (H), 14. (G), 15. (K)

33. FOOD FOR THOUGHT

1. Declan Rice, of West Ham United, 2. Southampton, 3. A pasty, 4. Paul Gascoigne, 5. Barry Venison, 6. Gordon Banks, 7. A slice of pizza, 8. Mark Fish, 9. a cabbage, 10. Tottenham Hotspur

34. CAREERING AROUND

1. Joe Cole, 2. Sir Bobby Charlton, 3. Gary Cahill, 4. Dennis Wise, 5. Ray Clemence, 6. Tony Cascarino, 7. Denis Irwin, 8. Nick Barmby, 9. Fabian Delph, 10. Scott Parker

35. PASSPORT CONTROL

1. Gary Lineker, 2. Tom Finney, 3. Peter Crouch, 4. Graeme Le Saux, 5. Stan Collymore, 6. Ryan Fraser, 7. Duncan Edwards, 8. Matt Le Tissier, 9. Martin Keown, 10. Trevor Francis, 11. Nigel Martyn, 12. Alan Shearer

36. GETTING SHIRTY

1. No 7, 2. No 1. (Numbers were allocated in alphabetical order), 3. Trent Alexander-Arnold, 4. 1993-94, 5. Asamoah Gyan, 6. No 99, 7. No 9, 8. No 9, 9. 1930s (1933, in fact), 10. Bukayo Saka

37. ON THE SPOT

1. Dave Beasant, 2. Robert Pires, 3. Oxford United, 4. Jorginho, 5. Manchester City, 6. Obafemi Martins, 7. Steph Houghton, 8. Gary Bailey, 9. Swansea City, 10. Jadon Sancho

38. SET YOUR SAT-NAV

1. (M), 2. (E), 3. (I), 4. (B), 5. (D), 6. (G), 7. (L), 8. (H), 9. (J), 10. (K), 11. (C), 12. (N), 13. (F), 14. (O), 15. (A)

39. WAY IN

1. Portman Road, Ipswich, 2. Dean Court, Bournemouth, 3. Amex Stadium, Brighton, 4. Kenilworth Road, Luton, 5. Cardiff City Stadium, 6. Plough Lane, AFC Wimbledon, 7. Wembley, 8. Anfield, Liverpool, 9. Fratton Park, Portsmouth, 10. St Mary's Stadium, Southampton

40. FRAUGHT FINALE

1. Bobby Zamora, 2. Huddersfield Town, 3. Charlton Athletic, 4. Blackpool, 5. Sheffield Wednesday, 6. Levi Colwill, 7. Crystal Palace, 8. Chelsea, 9. Birmingham City, 10. Dagenham & Redbridge

41. CREATURE CURIOSITIES

1. Lion of Vienna, 2. West Ham United, 3. Ted Drake, 4. Wolverhampton Wanderers, 5. Peter Bonetti, 6. Germany, 7. Peter Swan, 8. Mad Dog, 9. Darren Peacock, 10. Chelsea

42. ONE-CAP WONDERS

1. Tommy Smith, 2. Chris Sutton, 3. Steve Perryman, 4. Chris Kirkland, 5. Mike Phelan, 6. Ryan Shawcross, 7. Brian Little, 8. David Nugent, 9. Charlie George, 10. Joey Barton, 11. Kevin Davies, 12. Danny Wallace, 13. John Hollins, 14. Nigel Spink, 15. Brian Marwood

43. CITY SLICKERS

1. Birmingham City, 2. Manchester City, 3. Norwich City , 4. Leicester City. 5. Stoke City, 6. Bristol City, 7. Swansea City, 8. Coventry City, 9. Hull City, 10. Cardiff City, 11. Bradford City, 12. Lincoln City, 13. Exeter City, 14. Salford City

44. COMING OFF THE BENCH

1. Gary Lineker, 2. Teddy Sheringham, 3. Germany, 4. West Ham United, 5. David James , 6. Keith Peacock, 7. It is the most recent Premier League match in which no substitutes were used, 8. Duncan Ferguson, 9. Ruud Gullit, 10. Keith Gillespie

45. GOING TO THE MATCH

1. Emirates Stadium (Arsenal), 2. Pride Park (Derby County), 3. Carrow Road (Norwich City), 4. Amex Stadium (Brighton & Hove Albion), 5. Bloomfield Road (Blackpool), 6. Home Park (Plymouth Argyle), 7. New Meadow (Shrewsbury Town), 8. St James Park (Newcastle United), 9. Abbey Stadium (Cambridge United), 10. Turf Moor (Burnley), 11. Christie Park (Morecambe), 12. Madejski Stadium (Reading)

46. 2022, QATAR

1. Tottenham Hotspur's Hugo Lloris, 2. Julián Álvarez, 3. Emiliano Martínez, 4. None, 5. Wembley, 6. Arsenal, 7. Liverpool.

47. OWN GOALS

1. Tammy Abraham, 2. Sunderland, 3. Chris Nicholl, 4. Tottenham Hotspur, 5. Wolverhampton Wanderers, 6. Norwich City, 7. Coventry City, 8. Liverpool, 9. Luton Town, 10. Dave Ewing

48. HAT-TRICK HEROES

1. Sadio Mané, 2. Sir Geoff Hurst, 3. Jimmy Greaves, 4. Stan Mortensen, 5. Theo Walcott, 6. Dixie Dean, 7. Speedie for Coventry City and Slaven for Middlesbrough, 8. Malcolm Macdonald, 9. Bournemouth, 10. Trevor Francis

49. GLOBAL VISION

1. 2006, Germany, 2. 1982, Spain, 3. 1998, France, 4. 2018, Russia, 5. 2010, South Africa, 6. 1970, Mexico, 7. 1990, Italy, 8. 2014, Brazil, 9. 1958, Sweden, 10. 2022, Qatar, 11. 1986, Mexico, 12. 1962, Chile

50. I'M A CELEBRITY...

1. Andy Murray, 2. Ant McPartlin, 3. Usain Bolt, 4. Cilla Black, 5. Emmanuel Macron, 6. John Cleese, 7. Peter Cook, 8. Damian Lewis, 9. Ed Sheeran, 10. Ian Botham, 11. Keir Starmer, 12. Ken Dodd, 13. Frank Bruno, 14. Olly Murs, 15. Robbie Williams, 16. Tony Blair, 17. Liam Gallagher, 18. Roger Federer, 19. Rod Stewart, 20. Steve Cram, 21. Daley Thompson, 22. Elton John, 23. Matt Smith, 24. Tony McCoy, 25. Ben Stokes, 26. Serena Williams

51. PUT YOUR SHIRT ON IT

1. Liverpool, 2. Tottenham Hotspur, 3. West Ham United, 4. Chelsea, 5. Norwich City, 6. Everton, 7. Crystal Palace, 8. Manchester City, 9. Birmingham City, 10. Leeds United, 11. Southampton, 12. Coventry City

52. HAPPY FAMILIES (PART 2)

1. Eastham, 2. Manchester United: Brian and Jimmy Greenhoff in 1977; Gary and Phil Neville in 1999, 3. Bobby Gould. His son is Jonathan Gould, 4. Fulham and Brentford, 5. Sone Aluko and Eni Aluko, 6. Sierra Leone, 7. Alan James Ball, 8. Ghana (Kevin-Prince Boateng) and Germany (Jérôme Boateng), 9. Hereford United, 10. Jack Charlton (Middlesbrough) and Sir Bobby Charlton (Preston North End)

53. IN THE DOCK

1. Arsenal, 2. Manchester United, 3. Middlesbrough, 4. Chesterfield, 5. Portsmouth, 6. Luton Town, 7. Leeds United, 8. Rotherham United, 9. Wayne Rooney, 10. Sunderland

54. BEYOND THE BOUNDARY

1. Sir Geoff Hurst, 2. Arnie Sidebottom, 3. Doncaster Rovers, 4. Clare Taylor, 5. Scunthorpe United, 6. Northampton Town, 7. Andy Goram, 8. Bramall Lane and Kennington Oval, 9. Jim Standen, 10. Willie Watson

55. DOWN ON THE FARM

1. Stoke City, 2. Lionel Messi, 3. Gander, 4. Steve Bull, 5. Geoff Horsfield, 6. Southend United, 7. Stockport County, 8. Ipswich Town, 9. David Hay, 10. West Bromwich Albion

56. I'M IN CHARGE

1. Graham Poll, 2. Paolo Di Canio, 3. Mark Clattenburg, 4. Clive Thomas, 5. Michael Oliver – his wife Lucy Oliver was the referee, 6. Johnny Heitinga, 7. Jeff Winter, 8. Jack Taylor, 9. Pierluigi Collina, 10. Great Bookham

57. UNITED NATIONS' FLAG DAYS

Arsenal - 2003

Chelsea - 2005

Leicester - 2016

Liverpool - 2020

Manchester City - 2012

Manchester United - 1999

58. COLOUR-CODED

1. Andy Gray, 2. John White, 3. Rob Green, 4. Kingsley Black, 5. David Gold, 6. Lucy Bronze, 7. Manchester United, 8. Stefan Schwarz, 9. Charlton Athletic, 10. Wayne Brown, 11. Danny Rose, 12. Laurent Blanc

59. DID THAT REALLY HAPPEN?

1. Elland Road, Leeds (E), 2. Gay Meadow, Shrewsbury (H), 3. Boothferry Park, Hull (F), 4. Stadium of Light, Sunderland (B), 5. Highbury, home of Arsenal (J), 6. St Andrew's, Birmingham (I), 7. Holker Street, Barrow (D), 8. Ayrsome Park, Middlesbrough (C), 9. The Valley, Charlton (K), 10. Sealand Road, Chester (G), 11. Tannadice Park, home of Dundee United (A), 12. St James Park, Exeter (L)

60. BROWNIE POINTS

1. Wes Brown, 2. Ken Brown, 3. Craig Brown, 4. Rachel Brown-Finnis, 5. Michael Brown, 6. Bill Brown, 7. Sandy Brown, 8. Phil Brown, 9. Ally Brown, 10. Scott Brown

61. HY-FUN

1. Trent Alexander-Arnold, 2. James Ward-Prowse, 3. Stoke City, 4. Allan Saint-Maximin, 5. Ian Storey-Moore, 6. Callum Hudson-Odoi, 7. Hal Robson-Kanu, 8. Arsenal, 9. Shaun Wright-Phillips, 10. Bailey Peacock-Farrell

62. GLOVE STORY

1. Pat Jennings, 2. Faroe Islands, 3. Bert Trautmann, 4. Gordon Banks and Peter Shilton, 5. Mary Earps, 6. Mark Schwarzer, 7. Mike Walker, 8. Ronnie Simpson, 9. Brad Friedel, 10. Shay Given

63. 2003, SKOPJE, MACEDONIA

1. 17 (and 317 days), 2. Michael Owen, 3. Everton, 4. Switzerland, 5. The United States, 6. Switzerland and Croatia, 7. 7-0

64. FIFTEEN MINUTES OF FAME

1. (M), 2. (O), 3. (G), 4. (C), 5. (F), 6. (E), 7. (K), 8. (H), 9.(A), 10. (J), 11. (L), 12. (N), 13. (D), 14. (I), 15. (B)

65. MATCH OF THE DAY

1. Gary Stevens, 2. Paul Robinson, 3. Dave Watson, 4. Bryan Robson (the second of those was better known as "Pop" Robson), 5. Billy Wright, 6. Alan Judge, 7. Simon Davies, 8. Colin West, 9. Paul Williams, 10. Tom Finney

66. NICKNAMES

1. West Ham United v Everton, 2. Arsenal v Wolverhampton Wanderers, 3. Bournemouth v Brighton & Hove Albion, 4. Newcastle United v Sheffield United, 5. Chelsea v Brentford

67. FIRST THINGS FIRST

1. (F), 2. (M), 3. (E), 4. (B), 5. (O), 6. (D), 7. (G), 8. (I), 9. (C), 10. (K), 11. (A), 12. (L) 13. (N), 14. (J), 15. (H)

68. AROUND THE GROUNDS

1. Stamford Bridge, 2. Birmingham City, who play at St Andrew's, 3. Fleetwood Town, 4. Old Trafford, 5. Rotherham United, based at the New York Stadium, 6. West Bromwich Albion, who play at the Hawthorns, 7. Charlton Athletic (The Valley) and Bradford City (Valley Parade), 8. The Crown Ground, home of Accrington Stanley, 9. Racecourse Ground, home of Wrexham, 10. Meadow Lane (Notts County) and the New Meadow (Shrewsbury Town)

69. COMEBACK KINGS

1. Barcelona , 2. Tottenham Hotspur, 3. Charlton Athletic, 4. Middlesbrough, 5. Diego Forlán, 6. Leeds United, 7. Watford, 8. Aston Villa, 9. Queens Park Rangers, 10. Sheffield Wednesday (then known as The Wednesday)

70. DRAW YOUR OWN CONCLUSIONS

1. Alan Ball, 2. John Stones, 3. Ron Flowers, 4. Wayne Bridge, 5. Mick Mills, 6. Gordon Banks, 7. Trevor Cherry, 8. Nobby Stiles, 9. Joe Hart, 10. Alan Shearer, 11. Peter Crouch

1. HANGING UP THEIR BOOTS

. Craig Johnston, 2. Arsenal, 3. George Weah, 4. Detective, 5. Fire brigade, 6. Daniel Agger, 7. Neil Webb, 8. Chelsea,). Barry Horne, 10. Philippe Albert

2. TRANSFER TURN-UPS

. Charlton Athletic, 2. Clive Allen, 3. Rangers, 4. Sol Campbell, 5. Everton, 6. Paul Ince, 7. Southampton, 8. Coventry City,). Odion Ighalo, 10. Tommy Lawton

3. UNITED FRONT

. West Ham United, 2. Sheffield United, 3. Newcastle United, 4. Oxford United, 5. Manchester United, . Peterborough United, 7. Leeds United, 8. Cambridge United, 9. Rotherham United, 10. Colchester United, 1. Carlisle United, 12. Sutton United

4. FALLEN FROM GRACE

. Boundary Park, Oldham Athletic, 2. Roots Hall, Southend United, 3. Glanford Park, Scunthorpe United, 4. The Hive, Barnet, . Bootham Crescent, York City, 6. Plainmoor, Torquay United, 7. Edgar Street, Hereford, 8. SMH Group Stadium, Chesterfield, . The Shay, Halifax Town, 10. Victoria Park, Hartlepool

5. RED FACES

. Wayne Rooney, 2. Trevor Cherry, 3. Alan Mullery, 4. Ray Wilkins, 5. David Batty, 6. David Beckham, 7. Steven Gerrard, . Alan Ball, 9. Rob Green, 10. Alan Smith, 11. Reece James, 12. Paul Ince, 13. Luke Shaw, 14. Raheem Sterling, 15: Paul Scholes

6. WAIT FOR IT!

. The final of the 2019-20 competition (delayed by the Covid pandemic) and then, a day later, the 2020-21 final, 2. The enalty spot had disappeared under mud and needed to be repainted before Derby could take a spot kick (which they onverted), 3. Leyton Orient, 4. Jimmy Greaves, 5. 1961, 6. Tottenham Hotspur, 7. Manchester United, 8. The 2014 World Cup, . 1962-63, 10. A suspicious package was found at the ground causing a security alert

7. O' MY WORD

. John O'Shea, 2. Martin O'Neill, 3. David O'Leary, 4. John O'Hare, 5. Gary O'Neil, 6. Kevin O'Callaghan, . Frank O'Farrell, 8. Andy O'Brien, 9. Michael O'Neill, 10. Peter O'Sullivan (the commentator was Peter O'Sullevan)

8. NATIONAL PARKS

. (J) Wycombe Wanderers, 2. (D) Carlisle United, 3. (A) Dundee, 4. (G) Stockport County, 5. (E) Blackburn Rovers, 6. (L) ortsmouth, 7. (F) Everton, 8. (N) Plymouth Argyle, 9. (B) Kilmarnock, 10. (K) Crystal Palace, 11. (C) Ayr United, . (M) Exeter City, 13. (I) Aston Villa, 14. (H) Port Vale

9. WHAT'S MY LINE?

. Terry Butcher, 2. Crystal Palace, 3. Graham Potter, 4. Joe Baker, 5. Brighton & Hove Albion, 6. Ryan Mason, 7. Paul Mariner, . Aston Villa and Birmingham City, 9. Goalkeeper, 10. Paul Cook

10. CLIMATE CONTROL

. Sun Jihai, 2. Watford, 3. Tony Gale, 4. Denmark, 5. Aston Villa, 6. Wrexham, 7. Scarborough, 8. Milton Keynes Dons, . Scottish, 10. Huddersfield Town

11. TAYLOR-MADE QUESTIONS

. Gordon Taylor, 2. Alan Taylor, 3. Peter Taylor, 4. Tommy Taylor, 5. Matt Taylor, 6. Maik Taylor, 7. Neil Taylor, 8. Ian Taylor, . Phil Taylor, 10. Shaun Taylor

82. 2005, ISTANBUL

1. AC Milan, 2. Paolo Maldini, 3. 8, 4. Olympiacos, 5. None, 6. West Ham United, 7. Saudi Arabia

83. TENANCY AGREEMENT

1. Maine Road, Manchester City's ground, 2. Leeds United, 3. Arsenal, 4. Upton Park, home of West Ham United,

5. Uefa banned them from using Loftus Road because of its artificial pitch, 6. Fulham, 7. Plymouth Argyle, 8. Chester City,

9. Carlisle United, 10. Brighton & Hove Albion

84. SINGING FROM THE SAME SHEET (VERSE 2)

1. Louis Armstrong; Gerry Armstrong, 2. Tina Turner; Chris Turner, 3. Michael Bolton; Bolton Wanderers,

4. Bing Crosby; Malcolm Crosby, 5. Kelly Clarkson; Chloe Kelly, 6. Nat King Cole; Andy Cole, 7. Phil Collins; John Collins,

8. Crystal Gayle; Crystal Palace, 9. Roger Miller; Roger Milla, 10. Ben E King; Ledley King

85. CROSSING BORDERS

1. Sierra Leone, 2. Belgium, 3. Ivory Coast, 4. Spain, 5. England, 6. Netherlands, 7. England (women) 8. Russia, 9. United States

10. Zambia, 11. Northern Ireland, 12. England, 13. Angola, 14. New Zealand, 15. Curacao

86. COMBAT QUESTIONS

1. Everton, 2. From first round to quarter-finals each tie was held over two legs, 3. Bournemouth, 4. It was a prisoner-of-war

camp, 5: The Khaki Cup Final, 6. Sir Stanley Matthews, 7. Arsenal, 8. Vivian Woodward, 9. Highbury, 10. Charlie Buchan

87. THE KEEPER HAS SCORED!

1. Jimmy Glass, 2. Pat Jennings, 3. Coventry City, 4. Peter Schmeichel, 5. Bruce Grobbelaar, 6. Asmir Begovic,

7. West Bromwich Albion, 8. Brad Friedel, 9. Alex Stepney, 10. Alan Fettis

88. WEMBLEY WIZARDS

1. Arsenal and Tottenham Hotspur, 2. David Jack, 3. Wolverhampton Wanderers and Burnley, 4. West Ham United, 5. Leyton

Orient (then known as Clapton Orient), 6. Harry Kane, 7. Germany, 8. Turkey, 9. Luton Town, 10. Aaron Ramsey

89. COMING HOME

1. Raheem Sterling, 2. Owen Hargreaves, 3. Singapore, 4. Cyrille Regis, 5. Luther Blissett, 6. Nigeria, 7. Fikayo Tomori, born in

Calgary, Canada, 8. Ipswich Town, 9. John Barnes, 10. Bill Perry

90. RECENT EVENTS

1. Arsenal, 2. Ilkay Gundogan, 3. West Ham United, 4. Roy Hodgson, 5. Luton Town, 6. Erling Haaland, 7. Fulham,

8. Emiliano Martínez (Aston Villa), Cristian Romero (Tottenham Hotspur), Alexis Mac Allister (Brighton & Hove Albion) and

Julián Álvarez (Manchester City), 9. Wolverhampton Wanderers, 10. Rotherham United

91. THE AWARDS CEREMONY

1. Terry McDermott, 2. Gary Lineker, 3. 1973-74, 4. Manchester United (Denis Law 1964, Sir Bobby Charlton 1966, George

Best 1968), 5. Scott Parker, 6. Ipswich Town: Frans Thijssen (FWA) and John Wark (PFA), 7. Chelsea, 8. Luton Town,

9. Michael Owen, in 2001, 10. Alan Shearer: with Blackburn Rovers in 1994-95; with Newcastle United in 1996-97

2. CLUB LEGENDS

Sir Stanley Matthews, Bet 365 Stadium, Stoke City, 2. Jimmy Hill, Coventry Building Society Arena, Coventry City, 3. Bill Shankly, Anfield, Liverpool, 4. Sir Bobby Robson, Portman Road, Ipswich Town, 5. Gordon Banks, Bet 365 Stadium, Stoke City, 6. Peter Osgood, Stamford Bridge, Chelsea, 7. Billy Bremner, Elland Road, Leeds United, 8. Dixie Dean, Goodison Park Everton, 9. Nat Lofthouse, Toughsheet Community Stadium, Bolton Wanderers, 10. Johnny Haynes, Craven Cottage, Fulham, 1. Jimmy Armfield, Bloomfield Road, Blackpool

3. BIG MACS

Sammy McIlroy, 2. Malcolm Macdonald, 3. Lawrie McMenemy, 4. Paul McGrath, 5. Derby County, 6. Wilf McGuinness, Rugby League, 8. Everton, 9. Centre back, 10. Burnley

4. CROSSING THE DIVIDE

Steve Bruce, 2. Manchester City and Manchester United, 3. George Graham: Arsenal. Terry Neill: Tottenham, 4. Billy Bonds, Everton and then Liverpool, 6. Alan Ball, 7. Paul Lambert, 8. Bristol - Rovers and City, 9. Owen Coyle, 10. West Bromwich Albion and Wolverhampton Wanderers

5. HONOURS BOARD

2018-19, 2. 1987-88, 3. 2012-13, 4. 1971-72, 5. 2010-11, 6. 1968-69, 7. 1977-78, 8. 2007-08, 9. 1984-85, 10. 1972-73, 11. 1965-66, 2. 1973-74, 13. 1966-67, 14. 1985-86, 15. 1960-61

6. 2016, KING POWER STADIUM, LEICESTER

29, 2. 11, 3. Sheffield, 4. Everton, 5. Fleetwood Town, 6. Manchester City, 7. Wales

7. STAND FOR THE ANTHEMS, PLEASE

Liverpool, 2. Crystal Palace, 3. Chelsea, 4. Newcastle United, 5. Leeds United, 6. Norwich City, 7. Manchester City, Southampton, 9. Everton, 10. West Ham United, 11. Sheffield United, 12. Coventry City, 13. Stoke City, 14. Millwall, 5. Charlton Athletic

8. FANCY SEEING YOU HERE

Swindon Town, 2. Millwall, 3. Barnsley, 4. Wolverhampton Wanderers, 5. Leyton Orient, 6. Leeds United, 7. Coventry City, Northampton Town, 9. Leicester City, 10. Manchester City

9. JUST JOHNSONS

David Johnson, 2. Andy Johnson, 3. Glen Johnson, 4. Seth Johnson, 5. Gary Johnson – his son is Lee Johnson, Tommy Johnson, 7. Harry Johnson, 8. Damien Johnson, 9. Ben Johnson, 10. Roger Johnson

10. LAST HURRAH

Matt Le Tissier, 2. Manchester United, managed by Sir Alex Ferguson, 3. Thierry Henry, 4. Kevin Keegan, 5. Sir Kenny Dalglish, 6. Middlesbrough, 7. Alex Oxlade-Chamberlain, 8. Crystal Palace, 9. Peter Schmeichel, 10. Coventry City

ALL ANSWERS HAVE BEEN RESEARCHED AS CORRECT AT SEPTEMBER 8TH 2023.

EXTRA TIME
THE REST IS FOOTBALL

Questions relating to the participants in the podcast of this name
(Gary Lineker, Alan Shearer and Micah Richards)

1   Which players were the most common England team-mates for Lineker (he
    played alongside this player 52 times), Shearer (43 times) and Richards (12
    times)?

2   Lineker finished as the top flight's leading scorer (or joint leading scorer) in
    three different seasons. For how many seasons did Alan Shearer achieve this
    feat?

3   Richards was born six days after Lineker and his England team-mates ended
    their European Championship campaign in West Germany with a third defeat in
    their three group-stage matches. What was the year?

4   Lineker and Shearer won a combined 143 England caps but only played
    together for their country three times, all in 1992: which nation did the pair face
    twice, firstly in a friendly (in which Shearer scored on his debut) and secondly in
    a Euro 1992 group match?

5   Who was the only player among the trio not to win the League title?

6   Of the three players, one has a middle name Lincoln, another has a middle name
    Winston and another has no middle name. Which is which?

7   Who was the only member of the trio to play for England as a teenager?

8   Which one of the three players did not win the FA Cup?

9   Which of the trio played football for Great Britain in the Olympic Games?

10 Alan Shearer scored a hat-trick as Blackburn Rovers won 4-2 at home to a
    London team in the Premier League in January 1995 – and then exactly the
    same happened against the same opponents later that year. Name those
    opponents?

1. **Lineker:** Chris Waddle. **Shearer:** David Seaman. **Richards:** Steven Gerrard. 2, 3. 3. 1988. 4. France. 5. Lineker. 6. Lincoln – Richards, Winston – Lineker, None - Shearer. 7. Richards. 8. Shearer. 9. Richards. 10. West Ham United

A huge thanks to

BRESBET

BresBet is a UK based online betting company launched in 2021 by a group of people who love sport. We want our customers to feel valued, enjoy dealing with us and know that we'll always look to accommodate their bets, large or small.

We announced our first brand partnership with leading racehorse trainer Fergal O'Brien in October 2021 and at the same time the stable's number one jockey, Paddy Brennan, became our first BresBet Legend.

Since launching we've been proud to sponsor numerous horse racing events and top-class greyhound competition finals.

We hope the small part we have played in the production of this football quiz book will help it raise much needed funds for the important work of The Jeff Astle Foundation.

bresbet.com

THE BRESBET FOOTBALL QUIZ BOOK

Written by Chris Coley and Bill Edgar

The profits from the sale of this book
have gone to The Jeff Astle Foundation.

Thank you for your generosity.

**If you have enjoyed this book, then please head to
greatquizbooks.co.uk to find the full catalogue of charity sporting
quiz books.**